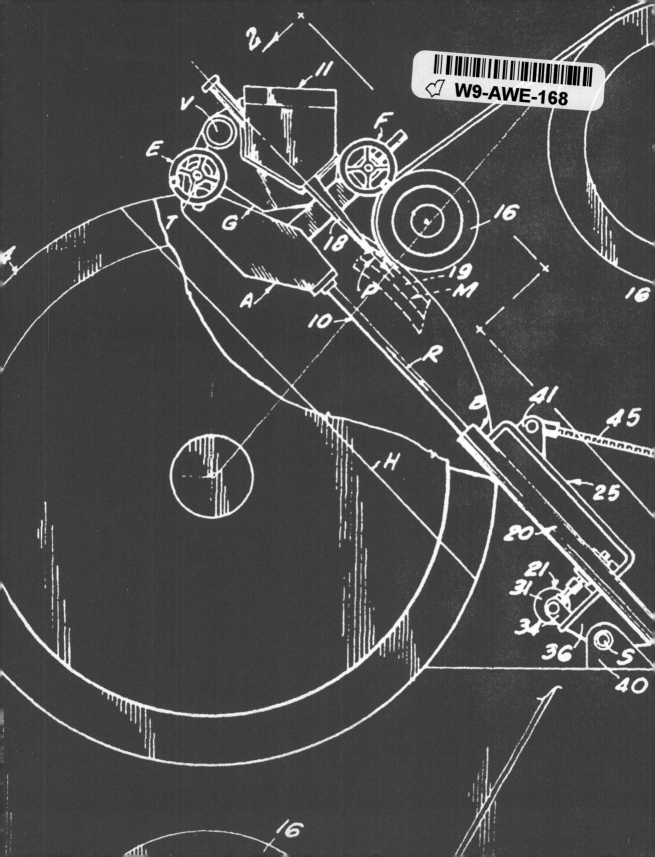

Chief Engineer

Chief Engineer

THE TRANSCENDENT LIFE AND CAREER OF SOUTHWIRE'S

Pete Cofer

by Vincent Coppola

SHOCK DESIGN BOOKS

454 Hamilton St. SE #12
Atlanta, GA 30316
www.shockdesignbooks.com

Photo credits: Unless otherwise noted here, all images are reproduced courtesy of
Southwire company archives. © Karsh, Ottawa, pg. 108: Museo Nazionale della Scienza e della
Tecnologia, pg. 16: © McNereney pgs. 58, 76, and 134.

Editor: Amy Bauman
Designer: Laurie Shock

First Edition

Library of Congress Number: 2013931106
ISBN: 978-0-9824779-5-3

Printed in China

13   2
8
3

Al

Aluminum
26,9815386

29

2
8
18
1

Cu

Copper
63.546

Preface

One day when I was about twenty-one, my Southwire job took me to meet with Mr. Pete Cofer and some others in his office on the fourth floor, that stronghold of Southwire's infidel engineers, all of them his zealous lieutenants. I don't recall the brief, except that we were seeking his permission or blessing on something. It was like going to meet the Pope.

When the meeting was over, we all left his office, but Cofer called me back in. He was standing there looking directly at me — this giant, accomplished man. I had never seen him at a loss for words before.

"Look," he finally said. "I want you to call me Pete. Everyone else does, and I don't like being called Mr. Cofer."

It was not a request.

"Yes, sir," I replied.

With those awkward words, we began a relationship that would shape me in innumerable ways and change the course of our company and industry. When I was a boy, I had observed Cofer from afar as an important Southwire leader, but I didn't know him or much about what he did. I knew he was our top engineer — our Chief Engineer. And that he cussed a lot and worked all the time: the first-in in the morning, and the last to leave at night. Later, I would come to realize that I didn't know much about him because he never talked about what he did. His results spoke for him.

Pete was a physically tall and imposing man's man, and he used charm and humor and his personal integrity to make himself approachable. He could be stubbornly strong-minded and, often, less than articulate about the abstract or emotional. But all of his skills came into sharp focus, powerful and precise, when working on business or technical challenges. I have seen whole rooms full of engineers from top companies around the world give Pete their worshipful attention all day long. As an engineer, Pete was always what you wanted to be when and if you ever grew up.

My affection for him continues even now, deepened by time and my recollection of the other important roles he played. When I went to work for the company, we were besieged by angry bankers who saw no way that Southwire could meet its obligations. The company was edging toward bankruptcy. My father, my hero and the most important man in my life, retreated into his own private life of longer and longer workdays, fearful of losing his entire personal fortune and forty years of hard work.

Something you always knew with Pete was that, when the chips were down, when faced with a gigantic business problem—or when the other side put up a whole room of their top people against you, if Pete was with you, you were always the intellectual equal of the challenge. He could not be outthought or outfoxed. He brought all of that to bear on the company's early 1980s financial crisis, and today we owe homage to Pete for our salvation.

In the background, SCR (Southwire Continuous Rod) technology sales took off and soared for Southwire, mainly because Pete sought running room outside of cable-making to apply his technical savvy and entrepreneurship. He was a rogue vice president in every way: unmanageable and hardheaded. And it worked, for him and for us. As he thrived, his band of merry engineers helped the company expand all over the globe. Today's reality, that two-thirds of the people on this earth enjoy light and heat and water from the fruits of Pete Cofer's intellect and energy, is just part of the testament to this man.

This little book pays tribute to this father, friend, and leader: Southwire's first *Chief Engineer*.

—Roy Richards Jr.
2012

Prologue

It was a scene repeated in every city, town, and hamlet in the United States: a young soldier arrives home from the war, seemingly indistinguishable from tens of thousands of others who'd spent long years in North Africa, Europe, and the Pacific Theater. This one a Marine, very tall, dressed in his green service uniform, standard khaki shirt, and tie. He wore glasses and, on his head, the soft garrison cap known familiarly in the military as a "piss cutter." He stepped off the Southeastern Stages bus in Wadley, a flyspeck lumber town in the middle of Georgia, after a four-hundred-mile trip from Camp Lejeune, North Carolina, that must have seemed like an eternity. He stretched his lanky body, blinked in the bright sunlight, and looked up and down the unpopulated Main Street. It was Sunday afternoon, his sister recalled. Reaching into his pocket for a coin, he called his parents who lived a few blocks from the bus station on Oak Lane Road. His mother's cry of joy burst through the phone. Her only son was home safe and sound. Jauntily, he swung his duffel bag over his shoulder, lit a cigarette, and waited for his father to come for him in the family's Buick sedan.

The Marine was one of more than fifteen million soldiers discharged after World War II — men whose wanderlust had been sated in the jungles of Iwo Jima, Peleliu, or the bloody sand of the Kasserine Pass, Anzio, and Omaha Beach. They married quickly, many to hometown girls who'd waited for them for more than four years, and started families. The more ambitious among them used the GI Bill to jumpstart their dreams and ambitions. Most of them were able to put the sorrow of war behind them although more than 405,000 Americans never made it home.

These were humble warriors who never bragged of their exploits and buried what they wished forgotten in the soft but fragile folds of the unconscious. Over time, they were revisited inevitably by horrors and loss they could not share. As the years passed and their fellow countrymen grew softer and less sure of their way, these veterans would remain steadfast. They were christened "The Greatest Generation," an honor commensurate with the magnitude of their successes and the depth of their sacrifice.

This Marine, a staff sergeant, squinting in the sunlight outside the bus station, was like them but different. He was returning from an extraordinary deployment in China as that seething nation experienced the birth pangs of the postwar world, an experience that would shape him for the rest of his life.

Like many returning vets, Daniel Baxter "Pete" Cofer didn't have much in the way of possessions: his spare uniforms, his ribbons and keepsakes, gifts for his parents and two sisters, and a few hundred dollars or so in severance pay. He quickly realized there were few jobs to be had in Wadley (population 2,000) outside the mosquito-bitten, snake-ridden lumber camps. What businesses that did exist, groceries and sawmills and such, had an alarming tendency to disappear in flames, to the point that the Wadley City Council passed a law banning the construction of any new wooden structures.

What Cofer did have—and this is America's greatest blessing—was possibility and opportunity. And because of these attributes, he didn't stay long in Wadley. The tinkering and mechanics he'd loved as a boy had matured into a passion to build and design and engineer. He'd never read the poems of T. S. Eliot—he'd struggled with English literature in high school—but had he read them, he would have been struck by the lines in *The Love Song of J. Alfred Prufrock:*

"Do I dare? . . . Do I dare?"

Pete Cofer dared. The arc of his life, as it unfolded in an era of seemingly limitless horizons, would be both commonplace and extraordinary. In today's era, defined by fake reality and instant celebrity, he stands as proof that a worthy life need not be lived in the public arena. His generation, The Greatest Generation, stands in mute testimony to that truth and needs be given voice. More than sixty years have passed since he arrived back home that Sunday afternoon. And like so many of his comrades—who now die at the rate of one thousand per day—Cofer has passed on. But his can-do approach to life; his brilliance, courage, and decency; his fierce loyalty, patriotism, and love of friends and family—make him both avatar and epitome of his generation.

A man to learn from and remember.

PART I

BEGINNINGS

Daniel Baxter Cofer was born in Washington, Georgia, on November 3, 1927. He dubbed himself "Pistol Pete" when he was given twin cap pistols and holsters one Christmas. From then on, he was called Pete.

Chapter 1

This is my friend, a human being. You will treat him as such!

—Theodore Roosevelt Cofer,
Pete's father

PETE COFER WAS BORN IN WASHINGTON, GEORGIA, about halfway between Athens and Augusta. His given name, Daniel Baxter, disappeared when he was five years old, according to his younger sister, Nancy Cates. Upon receiving twin cap pistols and holsters as a Christmas present, he proclaimed himself "Pistol Pete." The nickname stayed with him for the rest of his life.

His parents, Theodore Roosevelt "Ted" Cofer and Mariah Hall Cofer, were both born in 1898. Ted received his primary education in a one-room schoolhouse in Washington and then spent two years boarding at Madison A&M, a vocational prep school. Two years later, he was enrolled at the University of Georgia. When two of his elder brothers were called up to serve in World War I, Ted returned to Wilkes County to manage the family farm.

Mariah Hall grew up in Crawfordville, Georgia. Her father—Pete's grandfather Francis Baxter Hall—was an Englishman, apparently a man of some means who first immigrated to Florida and then moved to Georgia. After the death of his first wife, he purchased a tract of land in rural Taliaferro County in middle Georgia. Hall later served on the Taliaferro County Commission, and his name is inscribed with other notables (including Alexander H. Stephens, vice president of the Confederate States of America) on a plaque on the corner of the county courthouse in Crawfordville.

When Francis Hall married Louise Wallace, she was thirty years old, an old maid by standards of the time. Louise, Pete's maternal grandmother, is remembered for both her fiercely independent streak, which was quite unusual for a woman in those days, and her kindness. Like many homemakers of her day, she had a black woman who served as a maid and housekeeper to assist her with household chores. The two became close friends, and when the maid, whose name is lost in the mists of time, died, Louise insisted on raising her daughter along with her own children.

Family records and remembrances are imprecise, but at some point, Francis Hall contracted an infectious disease, possibly viral meningitis, and passed away. Louise Hall remarried, this time to a local doctor named T. P. McElreath. She, in turn, died at an early age; by one account, of an embolism triggered by phlebitis. Dr. McElreath relinquished any claim to Louise's children—apparently, there was no love lost on either side—and moved on to Burke County. Louise Hall is also remembered for bequeathing equal shares of her considerable estate to her daughter Mariah (Pete's mother), her other children, and to her quasi-adopted black child. "Grandmother Louise considered that girl her own child," remembered Nancy Cates, Pete Cofer's sister. "She made sure they all inherited the same thing."

Orphaned at age ten, Mariah and her siblings went to live with their Aunt Cecelia "Seely," Mrs. Jim Asbury, in Crawfordville, Georgia. When she came of age, Mariah had her own income, and, like her mother, possessed an independent streak. Francis Hall, her father, had left her shares in a British coal mine that brought her semiannual dividends right up until World War II, when she would have been in her forties. Mariah attended Maryville College, a liberal arts school in the Smoky Mountain town of Maryville, Tennessee. Founded as a Presbyterian seminary, Maryville College was integrated from its earliest days. Records show a former slave named George Erskine studied there as early as 1819.

Mariah Hall returned to Crawfordville after graduation as a teacher. She was later named principal of a small school in Screven County. Family members cannot recall how Ted Cofer met Mariah, but the attraction would have been mutual and obvious. She was tall, slender, and attractive; he was well built and stood over six feet tall, though quiet and gentle in demeanor. Mariah would later joke about her husband's premature baldness: "He looks so neat when he wakes up in the morning!" Ted told his wide-eyed granddaughters that he went bald from baby Pete "dancing on my head."

Ted Cofer traveled the state designing and building sawmills, planing mills, and the dry kilns used by the lumber industry to dry and season lumber. In the Jim Crow world of the working-class Southerner, Mr. Cofer stood out as a man who was willing to break the "rules" when they were at odds with his personal beliefs. "One time, Daddy and three men were working on a boiler," recalled his youngest daughter Nancy, eighty years old and sprightly in 2011. "They were building a dry kiln. Something went wrong, the boiler exploded, and the steam burned them. They all showed up at the hospital in Millen. My mother came, too. Daddy had a few spots on his body, and the doctors treated those. But one of the other workers, a black man, was severely burned. At one point, Daddy sent Mother back to the operating room to check on him. The doctor, notorious for a bad temper, was peeling the skin off this man without any anesthesia. Mother ran back to Daddy and told him what was happening. This doctor was a powerful, influential man. Daddy was a big, strong man. He went back into the operating room, grabbed the doctor by the collar, scrunched him up, and shouted, 'This is my friend, a human being, and you will treat him as such!'" Old grudges die hard in small towns. All these years later, Nancy Cates refuses to name the offending doctor because both families still have roots in the area.

Ted and Mariah lost their first child, a boy, at birth. At delivery, the umbilical cord was discovered wrapped around the newborn's neck. Ted had been out of town building a mill in White Plains (population approximately 200) in east Georgia. He was devastated and made sure his next three children, Theodora (named for him), Daniel Baxter ("Pete"), and Nancy all thrived. Each time Mariah came to term, Ted moved his family in with his parents in Rayle, outside Washington. All three were delivered by Dr. Charles Wills at Washington General Hospital.

Ted Cofer moved the family to Millen after he was contracted to build a mill for the Wasden Lumber Company. Not long after completion, that mill caught fire (a ghostly reenactment of the devastation Sherman wrought in December of 1864) and burned to the ground. Ted Cofer started again, this time locating the facility on the edge of town. He, Mariah, and the children began to put down roots for an extended stay.

Pete and his sisters grew up in Millen, another sunbaked flyspeck in southeast Georgia. When Pete was a boy, Cotton Avenue (the main thoroughfare) consisted of a single row of houses facing the railroad tracks. Millen had the misfortune of being home to Camp Lawton, a notorious Confederate POW camp, and being directly in the path of General Sherman's march to Savannah. The town was burned, as the histories note, "with little sympathy."

Pete's family moved to Millen, Georgia, where Pete (above, middle) where he attended Sunday school, saved a childhood friend from drowning, and, after finishing tenth grade, "souped up" a 1937 Model 60 Ford. He got it up to 110 miles per hour before the sheriff of Jenkins County pulled him over for speeding.

Young "Pistol Pete" with his sister Teddy.

CHAPTER 2

Santy Claus always came.

—NANCY COFER ON PETE'S CHILDHOOD

BY ALL ACCOUNTS, PETE GREW UP IN A SECURE and harmonious household. His parents were still exchanging love letters when they were in their fifties. The culture and values that shaped Pete are a snapshot of a small-town America that no longer seems to exist, a society in which hard work, honesty, patriotism, decency, and hope are living virtues rather than platitudes. He went to church, played football, worked odd jobs, got himself a car and souped it up, and fell in love with the girl next door.

This is an America brought to life through the memories of Ted and Mariah's surviving daughter, Nancy Cofer Cates:

> I remember my mother cooking wonderful Christmas dinners. Some of Daddy's family would come to visit us. Santy Claus always came. There were a couple of kids in Millen who wouldn't have had any Christmas. My parents invited them to stay the night with us. They had Santy Claus with us. . . . My father's favorite holiday was the Fourth of July. We'd have a big barbecue down on the Ogeechee River. The men cooked a big old pig. The women would make rice and hash and pickles and coleslaw. One of Daddy's neighbors had a place on the river. They would cook that hog all night long, sipping 'shine' while they were at it. Next morning, the young children would play in the river; the teenagers would be in boats. The big people would eat and smoke. It was just lots of fun. Such camaraderie. This was an era when everybody looked after one another. A really good era to grow up in.

Ted Cofer always had a passion for sweets. Mariah baked chocolate pies, pecan pies, apple pies, peach cobblers, and Jell-O topped with the rich fresh cream the milkman delivered each morning. People didn't count calories back then. You didn't monitor your cholesterol and blood pressure the way baseball fans track major league batting averages. *Atherosclerosis* was just a word with a lot of letters, but the disease would haunt both father and son in the years ahead.

Church was a big part of life. The Cofers attended the Baptist Church of Millen, and they lived next-door to the Methodist preacher's house. Pete had a perfect attendance record at Sunday school. One of the preacher's sons was handicapped and traveled up and down the street with the other children in a cart pulled by a goat. Unlike her tall, gangly brother, Nancy Cofer was the "teeniest kid in the neighborhood" and would hitch rides on the goat.

As a kid, Pete's offbeat sense of humor began to take shape. On one occasion, his sister Theodora, "Teddy," had committed an infraction serious enough to warrant a spanking from her father. Ted ordered Pete to go outside and fetch him a switch. Wary of his older sister's vengeance, Pete, trying not to giggle, returned with a "poppy stem." Frustration building, Ted then sent Nancy after one. No fool, she quickly realized, "I'd best not bring anything." Ted gave up on the switches, and he bent all three of his brood over the bathtub and walloped them with his hand. Instantly feeling guilty, he piled the kids into his car, drove to the Millen Pharmacy, and bought them sodas. "This was the first soda I ever had," Nancy recalled.

One night, Teddy, pretty and a bit vain, arrived home to find Pete parading around the house in her bathing suit. She shrieked, and he ran away giggling and screaming. She had to chase him down and pull it off. Another night, some kid—Nancy is sure it was Pete—tied a string to a dead snake, hid behind a car, "and wriggled it every time somebody passed by." He played with the snake, Nancy said, until "it was ripe."

Pete never mentioned his swimsuit debut as an adult, but he loved to repeat his pig's foot story. The tale can still be heard in various forms all over Carrollton. At the time, he was fourteen and working in a Millen grocery store. "Everything came in barrels," recalled Harold Miles, one of Pete's Carrollton buddies, swearing he heard it firsthand from Cofer. "You took your own container to the grocer, and what you wanted—meal or flour—came in a big barrel. One of Pete's regular customers was a black guy who loved pickled pig's feet, which were packed in a fifty-gallon barrel. You'd knock the head out of the barrel to open it and then keep it covered with a cloth or something. Well, this guy came in one morning and wanted his pig's foot. And he paid his nickel or whatever it was. Pete stuck a long fork down in the barrel. It came out with a drowned kitten skewered on it!

"The man screamed in horror, but Pete reacted quickly. In one motion, he tossed the dead kitten aside. The customer said, 'Mister Pete, ain't that a kitten?' Pete said, 'Yeah, but I thought you said you wanted a pig's foot?'" In some versions of the tale, Pete replaced the kitten with a rat. Pete's sister Nancy insists it was a kitten—specifically, the offspring of the female cat the storeowner kept on the premises to chase mice.

Both of Pete's sisters filled in at the Millen dime store on Saturdays. They worked long hours—8:00 a.m. until 11:00 p.m.—and were paid 15¢ an hour, with their lunch break deducted from their pay. Pete's big job was at Western Auto, where he rotated tires and changed oil in return for the privilege of driving the cars "up and down the ramp," Nancy recalls. He was a decent athlete, playing linebacker and offensive end for the Millen High School Red Raiders. Cofer played alongside a future Marine Corps officer and Southwire executive named John Chapple ("Chap") Chandler. The team went undefeated in Pete's senior year. At six foot four, Pete was the tallest player on the field. He apparently got his height from his paternal grandfather, Cornelius Randolph Cofer, a gentleman remembered as "being real tall."

In high school, Pete's interest in science and mathematics flourished. At one point, he knew more math than the eleventh grade teacher "and could help her teach," remembered Nancy. On the other hand, he was so bad in language arts that he wound up taking remedial eighth, ninth, and tenth grade English during his senior year. "I don't need that stuff," he grumped to his sisters. It was a complaint he'd repeat for the rest of his life, endlessly torturing his future secretary, Hazel Sprewell, with misspellings and grammatical errors.

In high school, Pete fell in love with a girl named Mary. She was three years older than he was. He carried her picture with him alongside those of his sisters and his parents when he went off to war. Like millions of May-December relationships, it went nowhere. Teddy and Pete graduated from Millen High. When Nancy was of high school age, Ted and Mariah moved their family back to Washington, Georgia. Ted soon left for Wadley, sixty miles away, to build yet another lumber mill, commuting home on the weekends. His peripatetic ways would manifest themselves in Pete in the decades ahead. The son would crisscross international boundaries the way the father crossed county lines.

Nancy graduated from Washington High School and then from Bessie Tift College (now Tift College), a private women's school in Forsyth, Georgia. Teddy followed her mother's path to Maryville College in Tennessee. Here was the American Dream made manifest: all three of Mariah and Ted's children would graduate from college.

After high school, Pete spent two years in Milledgeville at the Georgia Military College, a junior college. After the Japanese attack on Pearl Harbor in December 1941, like millions of patriotic young Americans, he enlisted in the Marine Corps and shipped out to the Pacific. He was on a troop ship when the first atomic bomb (code name: "Little Boy") was dropped on Hiroshima on August 6, 1945. When the war ended that September, Cofer was transferred to China. Among other duties, he served as a courier between the Allies and the turbulent giant's emerging political factions. The details, duties, and time frame of his tour in China remain vague . . . so vague that it's clear Pete consciously chose not to reveal them.

In the immediate aftermath of the Japanese surrender, the Allied powers were hoping to negotiate a truce between Chiang Kai-shek's Nationalist Chinese forces and Mao Zedong's surging Communists. A miniscule player on a titanic stage, Cofer saw firsthand the birth pangs of the Cold War and the fierce struggle between communism and capitalism that would dominate geopolitics for the next half-century. Barely twenty, he witnessed—though rarely spoke of—Chinese corpses piled up in mass executions, intrigues, and betrayal among all sides and factions. He watched history unfold, encountered a number of its major figures, and developed the curiosity and wanderlust that would drive him for the rest of his life.

Upon completing military service, Cofer returned to Georgia. He applied to medical school at Emory University in Atlanta and was rejected. He tried his hand at his father's timber business, but wrestling logs onto enormous transport trucks in the blazing Georgia sun didn't appeal. "He told me he was cutting wood all day and partying at night," remembered Milton Berry, an engineer who would spend many years working with Cofer at Southwire. "Finally, he woke up one morning and decided, 'Enough! I'm going to Georgia Tech!'"

It was a blind date that connected Pete to Dott Ingram, and within one year they were married.

CHAPTER 3

*Pete's favorite saying was,
"I'm not always right, but I'm never wrong."
And he meant it.*

— DOTT COFER

PETE COFER MET DOTT INGRAM ON A BLIND DATE. They married a year later in April 1953, a few months after he graduated from Georgia Tech with a degree in mechanical engineering. A vivacious twenty-two-year-old, Ingram had dreamed of an acting career but lacked the finances. When she met Pete, Dott was working as a service representative for Southern Bell at 51 Ivy Street in downtown Atlanta. The phone company's headquarters were a long football toss from the Georgia Tech campus.

On their first date, Dott, dutifully Southern, struggled to keep her own expansive personality in check. "I was a little bit reserved, not saying a lot," she remembered. "Pete talked, talked, and talked. His favorite saying was, 'I'm not always right, but I'm never wrong.' And he meant it."

Over the next year, Dott would also discover Pete's waspish wit—his endless store of either lame or off-color jokes. He was a man who could be very funny, to the point, Dott remembered, of being "aggravatingly funny." The humor, she sometimes suspected, was a defense mechanism. Pete was never one to share his inner thoughts and feelings. At times, her beau inexplicably withdrew into silence, the thousand-yard stare so often associated with combat veterans. "It was like he'd turned off a hearing aid. I'd talk, and he wasn't listening to a word I was saying," she recalled. Dott didn't realize that this was behavior familiar to the wives and families of men everywhere coming back from war.

Theirs was a whirlwind courtship, not unusual in those days. Family members say both Pete and Dott were eager to get on with life. While courting, they saw an occasional movie at the Fox or one of the other downtown Atlanta theaters (Pete loved John Wayne movies), made the scene at fraternity parties at Delta Sigma Phi, ate chili cheese dogs at the Varsity, and attended football games at Georgia Tech. That season, Tech, under legendary coach Bobby Dodd, was in the middle of a historic thirty-one-game-winning streak. At the games, the playing of "The Star Spangled Banner," Dott later recalled, "just raised the hackles on my neck."

If there was an unsettling note to what was otherwise a happy courtship, it was the call alerting Pete, then in his senior year, that his father had suffered a massive heart attack. Ted Cofer recovered, but over the next decades, he and two of his brothers would be debilitated by heart disease.

Pete's uncanny knack for being right, his nearsighted squinting over books and newspapers, his compulsive list making and note taking, his chain-smoking, and his insistence on dividing chores into "men's work and women's work" were attitudes and behaviors Dott would live with for the rest of her life. Even his marriage proposal, She recalled, wasn't exactly hearts and flowers. "I was hoping for 'I love you. Will you marry me?' Instead, he said, 'Will you be my wife and the mother of my children?'"

She paused at the memory and added, "You know, when I think about it, that was the highest compliment he could pay me." They were married in Saint Mark's United Methodist Church in Atlanta, a year to the day of their first date. A lovely reception was held at the Women's Club on Peachtree Street, just south of 14th Street and a few blocks from the Georgia Tech campus. They honeymooned "two or three nights" at the venerable King and Prince Beach Resort on St. Simons Island and then headed back north, spending a night with Dott's parents, G. O. and Clare Ingram, and another with Ted and Mariah Cofer.

The newlyweds had $300 in savings—scant money to buy furniture, pay rent, and eat for a month. They had a mattress and a bedspring, a gift from Dott's folks, but they possessed something much more valuable: a beginning. Pete had landed a job.

Wary of buses and crowds and trains and big-city commuting, and doggedly unwilling to relocate to a northern industrial city like Chicago or Rochester (at the time, home to Xerox, Bausch & Lomb, and Eastman Kodak) to ply his trade, he'd found a hen's tooth: an actual engineering job at Southwire, a wire-making operation located less than fifty miles from the campus. Southwire would be Pete Cofer's employer, his passion, and essentially his raison d'être for the next forty-four years.

———

In Carrollton, Cofer's new boss, Roy Richards, an entrepreneur who threw off ideas and innovations like chips from a buzz saw, was trying to grow what had begun as a regional construction company into an international powerhouse. In the years to come, Southwire, among other achievements, would revolutionize the manufacture of copper and aluminum rod, a vital component in wire and cable manufacture. To a layman, this may sound mundane or obscure, but it was a signal breakthrough that reverberated far beyond Richards's personal satisfaction and the domination of a lucrative, global market.

Like mythical Prometheus who gave the gift of fire to primitive man, Roy Richards would help deliver the gift of electricity far beyond the benighted South then undergoing electrification as part of the New Deal's Rural Electrification Administration. Under his leadership, Southwire would extend its reach not only to the international marketplace, but also to the struggling and impoverished peoples of the world. He'd help deliver light, clean water, and the energy to power factories, schools, and hospitals; it was a high calling in keeping with his religious faith and shrewd business acumen, but it was no easy task in rural Georgia where labor was unskilled and capital scarce. Roy Richards's dreams extended to the heavens, but to accomplish them, he had to literally "drag men from behind mules and put them behind machines."

CHAPTER 4

*I went down there, and they've got all these boxes,
and they got a Properzi machine, and I'm supposed to put it together.
And all the damn directions are in Italian!*

—PETE COFER ON HIS FIRST DAY AT SOUTHWIRE

WHEN PETE COFER ARRIVED AT SOUTHWIRE, Roy Richards was forty-two years old. Without doubt one of the most eligible and elegant bachelors in the Atlanta area, Roy had remained unmarried, consciously choosing to focus his energies on his company. Like Pete, he had served in the military—as an army artillery officer—during World War II and held a mechanical engineering degree from Georgia Tech. The Tech connection, which he held dear his whole life, was almost a sine qua non in his recruiting preferences. Indeed, he'd even talked one of his professors, Major A. A. Case, into helping launch Southwire.

One of the first persons Pete Cofer encountered at Southwire would have been the formidable Miss Margaret Samples Braswell. Officially she was Roy Richards's bookkeeper and secretary, but she was also a trusted counselor, confidante, and shadow chief operating officer who'd run the construction company and other ventures while Richards served in the military. A spinster until late in life, Braswell taught herself bookkeeping and accounting. Her filing system consisted of islands of documents piled all around her office that only she could navigate. She went on to become Southwire's secretary/treasurer. Simple, homespun, unimpeachably honest and forthright, Braswell was a shrewd judge of character and no doubt found subtle ways to bar the door to anyone she deemed unworthy of Southwire.

"Margaret told me she advised Mr. Richards when he was interviewing prospective employees," remembered Hazel Sprewell, who would become Cofer's longtime secretary. "She believed she could look a man in the eye and see what kind of person he'd be." Roy Richards signed off on Pete after their first interview. Margaret Braswell wasn't completely convinced. "She told me she didn't think Cofer would remain at Southwire," added Sprewell. "She saw how smart he was and figured he'd get bored and move on."

Roy Richards was equally smart and had precisely the kind of challenges that would keep a hard-charger like Cofer both interested and possessed. "My father was a very aggressive entrepreneur," remembered Richards's second eldest son, Jim. "At this point, he was determined to use technology to find ways to draw wire better, strand it better, insulate and deliver it better. And move on from there."

Roy also had his quirks and peculiarities. "Mr. Richards literally felt he had to live on-site," remembered Mike Wiggins, Southwire's executive vice president of human resources. "He wanted to be close and wanted his hands touching everything. He needed to know everything he could possibly know. He wanted to hear the machinery run. He had this insatiable desire to better the company, grow the company. And he always thought he could beat anybody. That part, maybe, was to a fault."

During a dinner party at Richards's lakeside home long ago, Charlie Loudermilk, the up-by-the-bootstraps Atlanta entrepreneur who built Aaron's Rents into a billion-dollar business, looked out a window and noticed row after row of young trees growing in perfect and magnificent symmetry. Mightily impressed and somewhat of a horticulturist, he stepped outside for a closer look. "The trees were *wired* to the ground," he recalled in awe. "That's how much of a perfectionist Roy Richards was."

When Pete left for his first day of work, Dott set about unpacking and setting up their two-bedroom apartment at the Tower Apartments. The new mattress and spring given to them by her parents hadn't yet arrived, and they'd bought a tired old sofa "with a letdown back to it" at a secondhand store. The bed was so unstable that Pete was forced to stuff his technical manuals under it to keep it level. "When it got unbalanced," Dott remembered, "one of us would fall on the floor. That's how we started out." The day went quickly. Before she knew it, it was suppertime, and she was scrambling to fix something to eat.

When Pete arrived home that night, Dott chirped, "How was work, Honey?" He glared and stomped around the apartment, firing up one cigarette after another, sucking the smoke into his lungs. "Oh boy, was he blustering and carrying on," she recalled.

"What's wrong?"

"I went down there, and they've got all these boxes, and they got a Properzi machine, and I'm supposed to put it together!"

"A what machine?"

"*Properzi!* And all the damn directions are in Italian!"

Roy Richards (left) was a forty-two-year-old bachelor when he hired Pete Cofer at his company. A true entrepreneur in heart and spirit, Roy was driven to make Southwire a success.

Currently displayed at the Museo Nazionale della Scienza e della Tecnologia in Milan, Italy, this early Properzi machine was invented by Ilario Properzi in 1949. It originally produced lead rod in a continuous casting and direct rolling system (CCR). The invention went on to process aluminum and copper, winning awards and revolutionizing industries worldwide.

CHAPTER 5

A Brobdingnagian assemblage of machinery—
furnaces, casting machines, shears, rolling mills,
cleaners, coaters, and coilers.

THE PROPERZI MACHINE SCATTERED IN CRATES AND BOXES across a ware-house floor was an aluminum rod mill purchased by Roy Richards from an Italian industrial designer named Ilario Properzi. In the postwar era, Properzi, based in the northern industrial city of Milan, had achieved a breakthrough in producing lead rod used in manufacturing bullets, ballast, shielding, etc. Roy Richards saw this process and thought it should be attempted for the casting aluminum rod, a primary step in producing stranded aluminum cable. If it worked, it could be a breakthrough for Southwire.

What Cofer found was a Brobdingnagian assemblage of machinery—furnaces, casting machines, shears, rolling mills, and coilers. The mill was intended to permit the continuous casting of aluminum rod, a step that would dramatically reduce time and cost, and thus boost Southwire's profitability. (The company's primary product, electrical wire, is manufactured from coils of high-grade aluminum and copper rod.) This rod is drawn, under tension, through a series of progressively smaller round dies, to reduce its diameter to make it easier to "twist" or "strand" together into cable. Copper wire is the familiar, coated wire running through our homes and automobiles. Stranded aluminum alloy cable, much lighter than copper, is used in the power lines that, among other industrial uses, deliver electricity from generating stations to our communities.

In those days, at Southwire and other cable makers, rod had to be purchased from long-established producers—Alcoa, Reynolds, Kennecott, among others—who in nearly all cases were Richards's downstream competitors. Alternatively, copper and aluminum bar could be "rolled" into rod in a labor-intensive and highly inefficient process that produced coils weighing approximately 250 pounds. Each coil then had to be "butt-welded" into a larger spool, before being drawn down into wire. The welds were time-consuming and susceptible to failure (particularly in aluminum power lines that, when strung through the treetops, were subject to rain, snow, wind, and ice). Production proceeded at a snail's pace.

Ken Kinard, who would work for many years with Pete Cofer, remembered the early mills: "The process was known as 'hot rolling.' We first cast and then reheated wire bar until it was glowing orange and sent it back and forth through a looping mill; it would go through, and the first sequence of rolls would make it a little smaller. A guy had to stand

Roy Richards was a calculated risk taker who knew he needed to develop new technological innovations in order to compete with companies like General Cable and Phelps Dodge. He entrusted Pete Cofer to lead Southwire to the next level.

there and literally catch the lead end—which was red hot and coming right at you—and turn around and bend it and feed it back into another mill. Then he'd step back and feed in another, and it would go through the looping mill. When I got here, you had to spend your first week on the job at the rod mill, a rite of passage. Down there, all these big guys were handling very hot stuff. Everyone had burn scars from trying to catch that hot rod of wire. It was archaic."

For Southwire to succeed, Roy Richards needed "bigger, faster, cheaper" technological innovations that would allow him to compete with companies like Essex, General Cable, Noranda, and Phelps Dodge. These giants, to put it mildly, had little interest in seeing an upstart from Georgia upset what was essentially a closely held monopoly. "Our hidden strategy was to get away from buying metal at producer prices because our competitors were destroying us in the finished products market," remembered Jim Richards. "Their metal was so cheap, and they'd make us pay-up for the metal. For example, we'd both sell aluminum cable to Georgia Power. They'd make a killing, while we'd barely eke out a slim profit."

Roy Richards anointed Pete Cofer to lead this charge. Purchasing an unproven Properzi aluminum mill was a risk, but Richards was, above all things, a risk taker who, over the years, would consistently, and on occasion, recklessly "roll the dice" to defend, fund, and grow his enterprises.

The innovation the Properzi mill promised was to make rod making continuous, delivering near-exponential increases in production, while cutting costs. As it turned out, the gap between "promise" and "delivery" was immense. In his 1966 presentation to the Newcomen Society for the History of Engineering and Technology, *A Southern Adventure in Free Enterprise/The Story of the Southwire Company*, Richards laid out his game plan: "If we were to succeed in our venture . . . it was imperative that our company exploit some of the industry-wide weaknesses we'd observed, and that had been instrumental in our decision to enter the wire industry. Mechanically and technologically, many things goaded us toward experimentation.

"Among the first things noted was that the method being used by our industrial contemporaries for producing rod, which was the basis for our product . . . was a slow piece-by-piece process. This was extremely costly for us and, if we were confined to this method, our stay in the industry was to be a short one. Southwire, unlike many of its competitors, did not enjoy the advantages of vertical integration, thus the margin of profit we could expect to gain on our products was to be slight. . . . It seemed only logical, therefore, that considerable thought be afforded the seemingly antiquated process of fabricating aluminum rod."

Years later, Richards's son and successor as Southwire CEO, Roy Richards Jr., remembered the Properzi gambit more dramatically: "It was a slingshot to use on the Goliaths of the wire industry."

Roy Richards was born in 1912 and grew up on a farm in Carroll County, Georgia. By the age of fourteen, he was running the family sawmill business and working eleven-hour days.

CHAPTER 6

Young man why are you in a hurry to electrify all these farms?
They haven't had it for a hundred years.

—AN ALCOA REPRESENTATIVE TO ROY RICHARDS

IN MANY WAYS, ROY RICHARDS AND PETE COFER were mirror images. Both struggled up from rural backgrounds. Richards, tall and strikingly handsome, was born in 1912 in Carroll County, then a place of exhausted cotton fields, red clay, and scrub pine, running west of Atlanta toward Alabama. When Roy was ten years old, family records indicate, his father, Thomas Wiley Richards, a "jack of all trades," lost his undercapitalized country store and farm equipment rental business. He wasted no time reinventing himself, a trait continuously expressed in Richards's family genes. Thomas Richards set up a sawmill on the unhappily named Dog River. As in all things Richards, it was a family business. Young Roy was put to work firing up the mill's boiler. By fourteen, he was running the operation, putting in eleven-hour days, and, as the former *Newsweek* journalist Joseph Cumming wrote in a profile of Richards, "judging at a glance the heft and character of those silent men who would appear in the clearing around the sawmill looking for work."

At fifteen, Roy Richards enrolled in the Boys Industrial School outside Rome, Georgia, a "work as you go" boarding school for working-class children founded by the philanthropist Martha Berry. The school is the scene of an apocryphal story told in the Richards family of a chance encounter between Roy, who was working on a tractor in the middle of a field, and a mysterious, well-dressed gentleman who "gets out of a long car." In due course, the man reveals himself to be Henry Ford, avatar of the American tinkerer, entrepreneur, inventor, and industrialist. A man very much like the future Roy Richards.

Two years later, Roy Richards arrived at the Fourth District Agricultural & Mechanical School in Carrollton, today the University of West Georgia. Principal Irving S. Ingram noted Richards's fierce intelligence and intensity and encouraged him to apply to Georgia Tech. He arrived on the Atlanta campus in 1931 on a scholarship, eighteen years before Pete Cofer enrolled. At Tech, Richards was mentored by Professor A. A. Case, who would later play a vital role in training and molding Carrollton's rural workforce into Southwire's skilled machinists and operators.

Both Roy Richards and Pete Cofer loved tinkering with machinery. As a teenager, Pete worked in a Millen auto repair shop and drove a souped-up '37 Ford that he bragged could clock 110 m.p.h. Not surprisingly, it did not take him long to run afoul of the local law enforcement. As he later told the story, a Jenkins County deputy pulled him over for speeding. The officer asked the fifteen-year-old Pete to open the trunk, perhaps suspecting he might be hauling moonshine. In those years, "shine" was hauled from the mountains of north Georgia in souped-up sedans very much like the one Pete was driving. (It was those drivers and their sponsors who began holding impromptu dirt track races near the Lakewood Fairgrounds, an undertaking that later gave birth to NASCAR racing.)

Cofer, who'd just completed a lesson on the Bill of Rights, refused the officer's request. In a squeaky adolescent voice, he cited his Fourth Amendment constitutional protections against illegal search and seizure. He then demanded the officer produce a "search warrant." Obviously the deputy didn't have one, but he had something more persuasive.

"I know your daddy," he drawled.

Pete, no doubt fearing "cruel and unusual punishment" in the form of a whipping from Ted Cofer, popped open the trunk. It was empty.

———

According to family records, Terah Richards, Roy's great-great-grandfather, was the only man in Monroe County to own a crosscut saw. (Terah is a biblical name, the father of the patriarch Abraham.) As Joseph Cumming notes in his monograph of Roy Richards: "Down through the generations, there is always evidence of this affinity for things mechanical, labor-saving and up-to-the-minute. Richards's men show up as blacksmiths, builders of covered bridges, operators of grain mills and threshing machines. They lived as if they had a rendezvous with the future when technology would come into full power."

Young Roy and his brother Hugh, aware of what the Wright Brothers had accomplished in North Carolina, built their own flying machine. This one powered by an old Model T Ford engine that, according to Cumming, roared to life and "went wildly bumping across a field. They experienced a hint of lifting off before they crashed into a tree, unhurt." For the rest of his life, Roy Richards would chase that brief moment of liftoff, the giddy exhilaration of leaving the dreary red clay and the gravitational pull of poverty and lowered expectations behind.

He founded the Richards Construction Company in the spring of 1937 and snagged a $118,000 Rural Electrification Administration (REA) contract to string power lines across 100 miles of Carroll County. Roy was twenty-five years old. Two years later, the company had run 3,500 miles of REA lines across the Southeast, reducing the standard installation time by 75 percent. He was already looking ahead—and back. (His father, Thomas Richards, had helped build and operate the first power generating plant in Newnan, Georgia.) In 1941, Roy was awarded a contract to build a power plant on St. Croix in the Virgin Islands.

After World War II, Richards ran into a wall. Conglomerates like Alcoa and Phelps-Dodge had a stranglehold on the wire industry. Richards, with a sheaf of orders in hand, was told the wait time for wire delivery was three years. At the time, an Alcoa sales rep quipped, "Young man, why are you in a hurry to electrify all these farms? They haven't had it for a hundred years."

Richards decided he'd manufacture his own wire. In 1950, he founded Southwire with scant capital, a pool of eager but unskilled workers, a remote location, no nearby raw materials, and little knowledge of how wire was made. More than most executives of his generation, Roy Richards understood the speed with which technology could level a playing field . . . how David could bring Goliath low.

A. A. Case, Richards's mentor at Georgia Tech, was a skilled machinist. Roy persuaded Case to move to Carrollton, where he began turning farm boys into heavy-equipment operators. Roy next recruited Roger Schoerner, a savvy young executive from Anaconda Wire and Cable in upstate New York to run the opera-

Roy Richards founded Southwire in 1950 with $80,000. Today, more than half of the continuous cast copper rod in the world comes from Southwire.

tion. He convinced a conservative banker named Arch Avery at C&S in Atlanta and another banker in Newnan to finance a big tract of land and a small factory. By 1952, Southwire had shipped 2,500 tons of electrical wire. It sales topped $500,000—solid, but not enough to survive against the giants.

In 1953, Richards hired the game changer: Pete Cofer.

One of Pete's first jobs at Southwire was to put together an aluminum rod mill that Roy Richards had ordered from Italy. The endless boxes of parts and instructions in Italian didn't stop Pete. Within three months' time, the machine was producing aluminum coil, which Southwire used to make cable.

CHAPTER 7

I was his wife. Southwire was his baby.

—DOTT COFER

THE GUTS OF THE PROPERZI ALUMINUM ROD MILL LAY scattered on the factory floor. Many years later, Jim Griffin, Southwire's senior vice president of sales, captured the young Pete Cofer "standing in an array of crates with a bewildered expression on his face," squinting at tech manuals in a language he couldn't understand. Though not for long. Pete's intuitive insight into things mechanical knew no language barriers, a fact he would demonstrate later in his career in scores of countries. Painstakingly, he began sorting out wheels, gears, shears, pulleys, gas lines and electrical connectors, scribbling notes and drawing diagrams until the behemoth began to come together.

Three months later, the melting and holding furnaces fired up, and the mill rumbled to life. After another several weeks of intensive troubleshooting and refinement, it was continuously turning out shiny coils of aluminum rod to be drawn and stranded into cable. No one had ever done this before. More than a technological advance had been achieved: Roy Richards's competitors' attempts to starve his fledgling company by denying him a guaranteed supply of material had been blunted.

The precise nature of the alchemy is unknowable, but Pete Cofer instantly and totally identified with Roy Richards's expansive vision. Perhaps it was the challenge of the underdog taking on the conglomerates, Roy's charismatic personality, Pete's embedded Marine Corps commitment to duty, a small-town boy's need to test himself against the best and the brightest, an engineer's vision of technology's promise, or the seductive glimmer of opportunity. Hunger, whether physical or intellectual, is a great call to action.

Roy Richards and Pete Cofer had a special synergy. Richards was dizzyingly entrepreneurial; Cofer was painstakingly precise and analytical. Richards would spin off concepts and ideas; Cofer would translate them into practical, real-world undertakings. "My father loved to write on a whiteboard," remembered Jim Richards. "He'd conceptualize something, and Cofer would sit there, taking notes. Inevitably, Pete would pull out his slide rule and work the numbers in an old-fashioned kind of way."

In the years that followed, Richards would give Cofer free rein with his research and development and SCR groups, scores of very sharp guys bivouacked like commandos around his fourth-floor office. "They had so many missions you wouldn't believe it," said Jim Richards.

Both Pete and Roy had vauntful egos, veiled, in Cofer's case, by quick wit and sour humor, and, in Richards's, cloaked in a peculiar opaqueness, as if the mortal being behind

Upon reaching the level of chief engineer at Southwire, Pete Cofer would accumulate forty patents.

the entrepreneur and the budding philanthropist was not intended for public display. "Mr. Richards was always something of a mystery," remembered former SCR team member Larry White. "You didn't see him that much, but you heard about him all the time."

Both men had aspects that were unknowable even to those close to them. In one memorable exchange in the course of researching this book, the former SCR engineer Milton Berry was asked: "Were there parts of Pete Cofer you couldn't know?

"Yes! I don't even know what they were!"

Through the '50s, '60s, and '70s, Cofer moved up through the Southwire ranks, rising to supervisor and then technical director, accumulating forty patents as he went. As head of the Wire and Cable Department—the heart of Southwire's core business—Cofer was integral in developing manufacturing standards and testing procedures, winning regulatory approval, and providing technical support and customer service. He would later be named vice president for research and development, and become a Southwire board member. And, ultimately, chief engineer," the most important title anyone could have in a five-thousand-person, technology-driven company.

CHAPTER 8

Your job is to get the job done!

—PETE COFER TO HIS TEAM MEMBERS

AS A MANAGER, COFER'S STYLE WAS GRUFF, straight ahead, a Marine storming a beach. He definitely had a temper and a short fuse, say his coworkers, as well as a way of cutting to the heart of a thing. He supplanted Thomas Edison's famous dictum on innovation, "There's a way to do it better—find it," with Max McGraw's, "There's a way to do it—better find it!"

Behind the gruff exterior, those same colleagues insist, Cofer was decent, generous, and even soft-hearted, but not to a fault. "If you told him it wasn't your job to do something, Pete would probably whip you and throw you out of his office," SCR team member Ken Kinard recalled with a laugh. "If you told him you weren't an accountant or engineer or purchasing agent, he'd say, 'That's right. Your job is to get the job done.'"

He'd happily sign up his team for any assignment in the company, often an assignment someone else was doing. "He didn't care," Kinard added. "I was just a tool in his workbox. If I got the job done before X got it done, he'd mentally check it off and move on to the next one."

Cofer never asked anyone to do anything he didn't do or hadn't done himself. Southwire is an organization overrun with hard chargers, but over the decades, those who were there insist Pete Cofer was the king of workaholics. "Pete arrived at 7:30 or earlier every morning," remembered Roy Richards Jr., who would later be named Southwire's CEO. "He was there at 6:30 every night. And the whole time he was working. Pete did not shoot the breeze. The pleasure that others get shooting the breeze, Pete got out of improving the system, dealing with an irascible customer, or beating the competition's technology with a better one of our own. These are the things that moved him. The whole building was dark at night. All the lights were off except for one office—Pete's."

Cofer's adolescent humor, playing tricks with dead snakes and such, transformed—in no small part due to the Marine Corps—from immature to outlandish. Everyone who knew him sooner or later fell prey to a wisecrack or an elaborate Cofer prank. For example, when Pete's international travels for Southwire expanded, Roy Richards's elder sons, Roy Jr. and Jim, were still straightlaced, postpubescent boys. Pete would dazzle them with snapshots of exotic beauties, assuring them the women were the daughters of eminently rich men to whom he was trying to sell a rod mill. "Typically, a beautiful, young Indian girl with a red dot on her forehead," remembered Jim Richards. "Pete would take me aside and whisper, 'It's all arranged, but you can't meet her until your wedding day. You need to get over to Delhi right away!'"

In Carrollton, Cofer got up around 5:00 a.m. to fire up his first cigarette of the day. By 6:30 a.m., he was sitting in Jerry's Country Kitchen, holding court as he ate biscuits and gravy and savored the first of many cups of coffee. Over the better part of three decades, Cofer regaled the Breakfast Club, an evolving group of regulars, with jokes, gags, and outlandish stories. Among them, the regulars were Harold Miles, who ran a local equipment leasing business, Carrollton mayor Tracy Stallings, banker Andy McGukin, the Reverend Allen Howard, and Roy Johnson who worked for the Georgia Department of Labor. The club was a moveable feast, journeying from a café in Carrollton's bus station, to the Green Front, to Jerry's on Newnan Street and later its Bankhead Highway locations.

The talk was sports and local politics, gossip, news, and whatever wool Cofer thought he could pull over his friends' eyes. "Once a year he'd bring us two or three pounds of country ham," giggled Miles, now in his eighties as he sat in the den of his home overlooking Carrollton's Sunset Hills Country Club. "He called it 'Promised Land Ham.' He swore he'd bought it in Israel! In fact, he had us convinced he bought it in Israel. He probably got it in North Carolina.

"Pete was the smartest man I ever knew," Miles continued. "He was more engineer than anything else. A brilliant engineer. Hell, most engineers are bright, but one-sided and one-dimensional. Pete could partake in a conversation with anybody from kings on down. He saw the comedy in almost every situation he was ever in. Most folks can't tell a funny story. Pete had his timing down pat. Looking back, 'Promised Land Ham' sounds ridiculous, but he had us fooled! He could also listen. If somebody had something to say, he'd listen, but he didn't suffer fools gladly."

Dott Cofer remembers the breakfast group as Pete's "real social life." She never took part in her husband's hijinks. No women were invited. This was a man's world, and Cofer was a man's man. Decades later, when Pete's health was gone and he still insisted on making the trek to Jerry's, Dott drove him. Another member of the group, usually Frank Jones, a Southwire executive, would drive him home. "I have no idea what they talked about," Dott said later. "I was so busy raising children, I couldn't worry about it."

CHAPTER 9

As with cancer research . . . there was no magic bullet.

—KEN KINARD

IN THE 1960S, ROY RICHARDS WAS SEARCHING for ways to offset Southwire's razor-thin profit margins, barely 1 percent in a good year—less than that of the average supermarket. He'd expanded his wire-manufacturing operations many times over, plowing profits back into the company and borrowing from an ever-growing number of banks, counting on increased sales and revenues to keep his creditors content. He'd also begun diversifying into an array of other enterprises, many not even tangential to wire making.

Long-term strategy involved expanding into overseas markets and integrating upstream; in the best case, controlling copper and aluminum ore still in the ground, extracting, shipping, processing, and smelting it. This was a huge and unlikely stretch, given Southwire's small size, the tremendous costs, and the chokehold the conglomerates maintained on the mining and transportation sectors.

Southwire's aluminum rod production had increased dramatically since Cofer had transformed the Properzi process (originally designed to work with lead, which melts at $621°$ F and is much easier to shape and mold than aluminum), but copper rod could still not be continuously cast. All of the challenges of the aluminum process were multiplied by the higher temperatures and greater density of copper. The work remained slow and labor-intensive, still processed using 250-pound slabs of bar, still being butt-welded together into coils, still subject to manufacturing delays, breakage, and quality-control problems. Complex engineering challenges were unresolved. For example, copper's melting temperature ($1,983°$ F), far higher than that of aluminum ($1,220°$ F), requiring heavier equipment—furnaces, rolling mills, edgers, casting wheels, coilers, etc.—than does aluminum. No metallurgist on Earth had mastered the process. Given that rod-making technology had changed very little since the Renaissance, many in the industry insisted that it could not be done.

"Impossible" was a notion anathema to Roy Richards. He sensed that technology was accelerating ever more rapidly and dramatically, faster and with greater amplitude, rendering what worked yesterday as obsolete today. Looking back, this absolute faith in technology that Richards shared with Cofer was a precursor to the thinking that would drive the world-changing "digital revolution" in the decades ahead.

Working with steel, fire, and molten metal, Roy Richards wanted a place in this coming world. But he was a realist, not a futurist. If Southwire failed to create a distinct technological advantage over its Goliath competitors, it would not survive. The challenge fell to Cofer.

"Pete's genius was taking a concept to reality," suggested Jim Richards. "He always understood the key issue, 'How do we take this little wire mill from the 1950s with thirty lookalike competitors, to international success?' The answer was to be radically different and do it through technology."

Since joining Southwire, Cofer had proved himself as not only a brilliant mechanical engineer but also a gifted metallurgist, toolmaker, designer—a man who intuited new approaches and innovations the way a musician constructed notes and then thoroughly and methodically tested and refined them.

In Milan, Ilario Properzi's own mills (today, Continuus-Properzi) had been adapted to the aluminum rod segment, but the Italians had yet to consider copper. Properzi agreed to sell Southwire what was essentially a prototype mill, but he would not guarantee its performance. "As the story goes, we got very little support out of Italy," said Will Berry, today president of Southwire's SCR Technologies.

Once again, Pete Cofer was in charge of assembling the behemoth. According to engineers who worked on the project, the Italian rod mill, while elegantly designed, was not up to the task. "It was like a fine Italian watch," said one engineer. "Or the difference between an Alfa Romeo and a Mack truck."

Roy Richards needed a Mack truck.

Among other challenges, Cofer and his engineers noted that the casting wheels on the Properzi mill would scorch and burn at high temperatures. Southwire retrofitted a copper alloy wheel to withstand the intense heat of the molten copper. Properzi's rolling mill (used to reduce or "roll" hot metal to a smaller size and cross section) was not powerful enough to shape copper rod. Cofer brought in the heavy artillery. He traveled to Worcester, Massachusetts, and convinced the owner of the Morgan Construction Company to adapt a heavy-duty steel rolling mill. Properzi's mill utilized a three-roll process; the Morgan mill, still used by Southwire today, is a two-roll system, simpler and much more robust—so robust that many of the copper rod mills Southwire went on to build are still running forty-five years later.

Retrofitting inevitably evolved into R&D, and ultimately, a new design. "After many trials and tribulations, Pete and his team got it working," remembered Will Berry, "but it was still not very good." Southwire produced copper rod on the Properzi mill for a couple of years, then scavenged what components it could and moved on. This unhappy parting with Properzi effectively became the basis of decades of complaints, recriminations, and legal wrangling—since settled—between the two pioneering companies.

To reduce development costs of a new copper mill, Southwire entered into a joint venture with Western Electric, the manufacturing arm of AT&T. At the time, Ma Bell was the world's largest user of copper wire, with a monopoly on all telephone lines and all telephones. There was a team of Western Electric engineers and a team of Southwire engineers. The work was done in Carrollton, and Pete Cofer was the lead guy for Southwire.

Western Electric, fortuitously, as it turned out, had no proprietary interest in the continuous casting technology. What it wanted was an endless supply of copper rod that could be produced reliably and at high volume and then stranded into the familiar copper wire found in every telephone of the era. "As with cancer research, it turned out that there was no magic bullet for the challenges we faced," remembered Ken Kinard. "It wasn't one thing, it was thousands of things: the chemistry of the casting wheel (a rotating copper ring that the molten copper is poured into), the water spray on the casting wheel that causes the copper to solidify . . . the band that binds the casting wheel so that molten copper doesn't flow onto the floor . . . Thousands upon thousands of things encompassing chemistry, metallurgy, engineering."

The SCR system using the Morgan rolling mill came on line in the fall of 1965, even then very much a work in progress. "I arrived at Southwire in April of 1966," remembered Milton Berry. "And it was an iffy process as to whether we'd make rod on any given day. We had a batch furnace that could process twenty tons of metal. When the metal got ready, we tried to cast it. If we were successful, wonderful. If not, well, we'd go back and try it again or cast it into wire bar when the SCR system screwed it up. This was not Properzi equipment; it was pure Southwire."

Nonetheless, production of copper rod on the new system increased to ten tons per hour. "At the end of the joint venture, Western Electric went its way, Southwire went our way," said Will Berry. Pete negotiated and got the marketing rights for the technology. Over time, those rights and associated patents would generate hundreds of millions of dollars in revenue and royalties for the company. They would make Southwire a name better known and respected in Guixi, China, than Gainesville, Georgia . . . in Bangkok, Riyadh, Istanbul, Mumbai, Tashkent, and scores of other cities around the globe. They would validate Richards's vision of Southwire as a source rather than an end user of technology. "Rod making," summarized Jim Richards, "allowed us to become a metal buyer, as opposed to a rod buyer. And that made all the difference for the future of the company."

SCR would also propel Pete Cofer, archetypal engineer with his bulging briefcase and slide rule, into world traveler, super-salesman, raconteur, emissary, and avatar. The greatness of Richards, Cofer, and thousands of men like them laboring essentially unrecognized in the gray shadows of the industrial world is that their success is not their own. In many ways, it is America's success: a tribute to the country's creativity, industrial might, and ceaseless ability to reinvent itself.

In the years ahead, Cofer would travel constantly, negotiate multimillion-dollar contracts, build relationships, and win respect from the shrewdest, toughest competitors in the world. He would, as his breakfast-club buddy Harold Miles predicted, "hold his own" with some of the most powerful political leaders and business executives on the planet.

Roy Richards's unwavering trust gave Pete the confidence to press the toughest deals, endure the most grueling negotiations, squeeze out the last bit of benefit to Southwire, knowing, should things go badly, the boss had his back. In return, the ex-Marine's loyalty was a given. Miles remembered his friend as "strictly a Southwire man. That's all he had his mind on. In return, Roy gave Pete total freedom. He went where the hell he pleased, when he pleased, as often as he pleased. Roy never interfered."

After three years of renting, Pete and Dott Cofer bought their first home on two acres of land in Carrollton, Georgia. It is here they would raise their family and live out their lives together.

CHAPTER 10

*Daddy, you never took us to Disney World,
but you take your Japanese customers to Disney World.*

—PETE'S DAUGHTER'S LAMENT

That's because you don't have a million dollars!

—PETE

ABOUT A YEAR AFTER ARRIVING IN CARROLLTON, Pete and Dott had moved from the cramped flat at Tower Apartments to a small house they rented from a furniture store owner named Groover. Two years later, they relocated again (Mr. Groover advised them that his grandson was returning from military service and needed the place), buying a house on two acres of land on Highland Avenue. The development was so new that the houses had no gutters and the streets were still unpaved. Pete and Dott would live there for the rest of their lives. Over the next eight years, Dott would give birth to four girls: Amy, Jean, Kay, and Ann. They had short names, Dott later said only half-joking, to better keep track of them.

The house expanded along with the family, with a living room, dining area, and a den tacked on over the years. Dott would later add a swimming pool. On the weekends that Pete was in Carrollton, he would sit on the screened-in porch smoking and sipping his favorite liquor, Jack Daniels. He may have seemed relaxed, long legs unfolded, but his mind was revving like a Chrysler Hemi V8 stuck in neutral, forever seeking ways to improve the rod mill, find new SCR customers, beat the stock market, and thwart the pesky squirrels constantly raiding the bird feeders he'd installed in the backyard.

"He was always trying to rig traps for those squirrels," remembered his youngest daughter, Ann Volle. Pete's initial tactic was to hang his feeders on long wires rather than poles. Undaunted, the squirrels would climb down the wire and raid the birdseed. Then he put grease on the wires and laughed uproariously when the squirrels fell off. From there, the battle escalated into a game of wits. Cofer, the great engineer, usually came up short.

He piddled around with golf with his Southwire buddy Harlan Carroll at the local country club, mostly because he knew golf was the preferred game of the business community anywhere in the world. In fact, golf would play a considerable role in his deal making when he began traveling to Japan. Though he could drive the ball exceedingly well, Cofer played golf the way Bobby Riggs played tennis in his later years: for laughs rather than lowering his handicap.

Pete and his mother, Mariah "Mamie" Hall Cofer, are shown here in front of Mamie's house in Wadley, Georgia. Pete is holding his daughter Kay, age five; Jean, age nine, is standing behind her father; Amy, age twelve, stands to her left, and Mamie is holding Ann, age two.

Pete grew roses and sunflowers in the backyard, but they withered away because he was always traveling—and his daughters neglected to water them. He also enjoyed woodworking, particularly building cedar chests and desks. But his soul was restless; he once described himself to Hazel Sprewell "as a man wild with ideas."

He spent many, many hours playing the stock market, scrutinizing stocks and tax-free bond offerings, picking the brains of brokers and consultants. Cofer kept what he supposedly learned to himself. (Like Roy Richards, Cofer found paying taxes excruciating.) He managed the trust funds his daughters inherited from Dott's parents' estate. In later years, Cofer had a percentage of Southwire stock awarded by Roy Richards to his top executives. And, by all accounts, he did very well.

He was famed for his frugality. On one occasion, after determining that the balance on his Southwire profit-sharing statement was off by a few pennies, Cofer marched up to the profit-sharing department (today's Retirement Plan Services)—he called them "bean counters"—and demanded a correction.

At home, he watched every nickel. "We never wanted for anything," Dott recalled, "but my husband did not like to spend money." She routinely shopped in Bennett's, a Carrollton clothing store where one shopper remembered the most expensive dress being priced at "around $15.99." The girls wore hand-me-downs, not unusual in big families. "I sure didn't like the hand-me-downs," Ann remembered, "because everything had already been worn three times before." Married with a child of her own, Ann has held onto her Carrollton High School prom dress because "it was the first new dress I ever wore."

Dott tells Pete stories with a widow's fond laugh and a shrug. She says her husband regularly refused to go on vacation, in part because he traveled all the time, but also because flying a family of six around could be quite expensive. Every so often, he'd relent, sort of, and pile the four girls—Ann squeezed into the front seat between Pete and Dott—into the car and head for Florida. Pete puffed away on a Marlboro while the other three girls, all knees and elbows, scrunched into the back seat. Somehow he managed to avoid Orlando's world-famous tourist attraction. "One year, one of the girls really got irate with him," Dott recalled. "'Daddy, you never took us to Disney World, but you take your Japanese customers to Disney World!'"

Pete's instant response: "That's because you don't have a million dollars!"

Throughout his life, he remained very close to his mother, Mariah, who, as mothers are wont to do, doted over her only son. His father would die of a heart attack at age sixty-two; Mariah Cofer lived to be ninety-two. No matter how much work or travel he had on his plate, Pete would make a point of attending family reunions in middle Georgia every summer. "Always in some really hot place," remembered Ann. Most likely Washington, Wadley, or Millen.

On Friday nights when he was in town, Pete would pile Dott and the girls into the car and drive the back roads down to Wadley, where his parents were then living, stopping at a diner in Senoia on a crossroad between Newnan and Griffin, and arriving at 10:00 p.m. "Didn't matter if the kids were teeny-tiny babies or three years old or whatever," Dott recalled. "Pete's parents were waiting on us when we got there with cake and milk for the children. Dott, who had a strained relationship with her own mother, loved Mariah Cofer, whom her girls knew as "Biddie": "She always treated me like one of her own daughters."

"Biddie was good-natured, kind, and funny," remembered Amy Cofer. "Always interested in what you were doing and present in the moment when she was carrying on a conversation with you. She didn't think the whole world revolved around her, so it was always fun to be around her."

While Pete had a jeweler's eye for engineering precision and detail, he seemed totally oblivious to his personal appearance. His interests lay elsewhere, perhaps at the intersection between concentration and obsession. With anything work related, Cofer was as demanding as a Marine drill instructor bouncing a quarter off a hapless recruit's blanket. "I used to try to pack his suitcase," Dott said, "but he waved me off. He knew exactly what he wanted. He had a list jotted down in one of his black books: 'six of this and six of that.' If he was going to be gone two weeks, he'd set everything out and get it done. He made copies of this list, and when he went on a trip, check things off as he went along."

One day, Pete showed one of his little black books to his third daughter, Kay, whom, he'd determined, was the "rebellious one" in the family. (In fact, in many ways Kay was just like him.) He'd just given her a dressing down after she committed some minor infraction, complaining, "You could never work for me because you're not organized!"

Kay, who was thirteen years old at the time, picked up the story: "I looked at his list. It was shirts and ties and shoes and socks, whatever. The very last thing said, 'Teeth.' And

I'm thinking, 'Daddy, 'if you've got to write to remember your teeth...'"

To Cofer, suits and ties, like slide rules, were simply tools of the trade—things he needed to get the job done. He wore them on interminable intercontinental flights because he feared his luggage might be lost, and a vital meeting missed. Despite his precautions, his bags went missing quite frequently, including one memorable time in Moscow when he was forced to don another man's suit whose pant leg came up to his shin. But he never missed a meeting.

"My husband had an Andy Griffith blue-and-white seersucker suit," remembered Dott Cofer. "That's what he wore all summer." Cofer's suits, shirts, ties, even his underwear were invariably scarred by cigarette burns. He once handed a stained tie to Hazel Sprewell, suggesting she boil it because "it would make a good pot of soup."

It was a clip-on tie. "I had to look all over everywhere trying to buy them," remembered Dott, "because he didn't want to fool with tying a tie." Clip-on ties were efficient; Pete was efficient. "I'd go see Pete and say, 'My dad wants to talk to you about thus and such and are you ready?'" recalled Roy Richards Jr. "'Yeah, I'm ready to go.' He'd walk over some place and get his clip-on tie. He'd clip it on and walk to my dad's office. He was transformed by that tie." Cofer triggered a near rebellion among his pocket-protector-wearing engineers when he bought clip-on ties embossed with the SCR logo and insisted they wear them, too.

If Cofer gave a nod to fashion, it was his choice of eyeglasses. He preferred a pair with heavy, transparent brown frames. In an era where black frames were de rigueur, his brown frames were doubtless "unusual." Daughter Ann suggested they were probably the cheapest ones available. He even claimed he was too busy to go to the optometrist, so he sent Hazel Sprewell, his secretary, to purchase them. "You know that's something you really can't do for another person," she recalled with a laugh. "I remember one of the times he sent me. It was a hot August day. I went and picked out a pair of frames and brought them back to the office. And he fussed around! He didn't like the frames! He threw them down! I thought 'Well you ... you, you know what! It's hot as Hades and me out there trying to get something to please you. And you don't like it!'"

He avoided regular visits to the dentist until he was in his fifties. He shrugged off warnings to eat healthy food and to cut back on tobacco use. Throughout his life, Cofer loved fried food and boiled vegetables. Dott often served him "cush," stewed corn, black-eyed peas, fresh tomatoes, with crumbled, buttered biscuits on top. A thick steak, pork chops or hot biscuits slathered with white sawmill gravy were close to his heart. As were chicken-fried steak, chopped pork, okra, stewed corn, yellow squash, collards boiled for hours in ham hocks flaked with red pepper—all of which are the tasty, heart-stopping cuisine familiar to anyone growing up in the South. "Pete could not abide finger foods," Sprewell recalled. "He'd go to his family reunions and brag about eating lots of 'them devilish eggs.'"

Overseas, he favored Chinese food. Cofer would scour entire cities hunting for a reliable Chinese restaurant. Failing that, he'd plead with whatever local agent Southwire employed to track down a pushcart, a vendor, anyone who'd sell him dumplings or dim sum. He had a particular aversion to Indian food, but nonetheless would become famous for eating, or drinking, anything offered to him while pursuing a deal.

CHAPTER 11

*Mr. Richards would come down to rod mill again and again.
Each time, he'd either shake everyone's hand or shake his head
and walk away wondering where his money had gone.*

—SCR ENGINEER NOELL WILSON

SOUTHWIRE'S PRIMARY BUSINESS IS WIRE MAKING. Still privately held by the Richards family, today the company manufactures building wire and cable, utility and industrial power cable, high voltage cable, and copper and aluminum rod (Pete Cofer's personal enterprise) and builds and sells copper rod mills in more than sixty countries. Today, one in three new homes built in the United States is wired by Southwire. In 1965, such success seemed improbable. The company's margins were small, its competitors fierce, its bankers never certain if the value of the vast inventory of aluminum Roy Richards used as collateral for his expansions would plummet like the Dahlonega Mine Train at Six Flags Over Georgia.

Early in 1965, Roy Richards, Pete Cofer, and dozens of "rail-hangers," watched as Cofer's baby, the prototype Southwire Continuous Rod (SCR) copper mill, rumbled to life. They'd gathered many times before and come away disappointed. The mill stretched one-hundred yards long. To an uninitiated observer, it was a behemoth—hot, noisy, dangerous-looking—that seemed to hark back to the beginning of the Industrial Revolution. At one end, an overhead crane began delivering baled packets of copper scrap to the gaping mouth of a rotating batch furnace called a "Doctor Thomas." Sweating men wearing safety harnesses to avoid tumbling into the 2,000° F inferno stepped forward and used oversized tongs to wrestle the scrap into the furnace now flaring a lurid green.

Cofer and Richards stood watching for nearly two hours as molten copper slowly moved out of the batch furnace into a smaller, temperature-controlled Ajax "holding furnace" designed to regulate temperature as the copper flowed into the next station, the casting wheel. The casting wheel and its associated belts, wheels, and motors (altogether, the "casting machine") were the heart of the Southwire technology. They were the real breakthrough. The whole affair, as tall as a steam locomotive and nearly as complicated, bore little in common with its Properzi predecessor. Cofer had applied the simple Properzi idea to much higher temperature metals, inventing a machine that could run almost endlessly at many multiplies as the little Italian gizmo's output, and at unprecedented levels of quality. And Cofer had coupled it together with all of its upstream and downstream components, creating a special-purpose, one-product factory for copper rod. It changed the company, the industry, and the world.

Emerging from the casting machine, newly formed copper bar passed through an edging station, where it was "prepped"—rough edges shaved—en route to the Morgan Steel rolling mill, which progressively rolled it into copper rod. From the rolling mill, the rod moved next to a bath of pickling solution that removed the oxides that had instantaneously formed on its surface. Then, scrubbed bright as a newly minted penny, the rod moved on to a coiler, where it spooled out as neatly as a garden hose.

Success!

To Richards and Cofer, each agonizing step must have seemed like the one-hundred-meter hurdles run in slow motion. They finally relaxed and congratulated each other as the first coils of copper rod were deposited—money in the bank—to be carted away and drawn into wire or stranded cable. The process was nonstop, continuous, never-ending. A watershed breakthrough unknown anywhere else in the world. A machine that would catapult Southwire to fame and fortune.

Of course, Murphy's Law guaranteed that breakdowns and setbacks would bedevil Cofer and Richards for the next five years, even as the rod mill's output climbed to more than twenty-four tons per hour. Pete Cofer's name would later be registered on more than forty U.S. and three hundred overseas patents, almost all associated with the continuous casting process. Among the scores of upgrades and improvements he and his SCR team would engineer, Cofer replaced the batch furnace with a one-hundred-ton-capacity shaft furnace fed by a mechanical loader that could deliver two-hundred-plus-pound "cathodes" of 99.97 percent pure copper.

Each improvement, a piece in a complex puzzle, required hundreds of man-hours, hundreds of thousands of dollars. "Mr. Richards would come down to rod mill again and again," remembered Noell Wilson, one of Cofer's engineers. "Each time, he'd either shake everyone's hand or shake his head and walk away wondering where all his money had gone."

CHAPTER 12

Southwire was central to everything down here. All my relatives worked for Southwire. If we hadn't, we'd be poor white trash out in the middle of nowhere, living out of double-wides or single-wides.

—LARRY WHITE, FORMER SCR TEAM MEMBER

IN THE SPRING OF 1965, LYNDON BAINES JOHNSON was serving his first elected term as president after defeating Barry Goldwater in a landslide. The Arizona senator was a favorite of Alice Huffard Richards, Roy Richards's lovely, Virginia-born wife. It was a season of change, with more tumultuous years on the horizon: the Vietnam conflict was escalating; Medicare and Medicaid were signed into law; Martin Luther King Jr.'s march from Selma to Montgomery, Alabama, got underway; and a young, impossibly upbeat Cassius Clay (later Muhammad Ali) knocked out Sonny Liston to claim the heavyweight boxing crown. In Georgia, the forward-looking Carl Sanders was governor; Lester Maddox waited in the wings.

In Carrollton, Roy Richards was literally changing people's lives. After World War II, he'd spearheaded a drive to build a Carroll City-County Hospital (today, Tanner Medical Center). He would serve as the chairman of the hospital authority for the next quarter century. "Everybody talked about Mr. Richards," remembered one longtime Carroll County resident whose family members worked at Southwire. "Mr. Richards was looked at very kindly among the churches and in the community. He had a great affinity among the black folks around here. He really went after them as an employment base on the plant floor. A lot of folks who couldn't get employment anywhere else were able to get it at Southwire. Mr. Richards's attitude was, 'If you'll work, you'll get a job.' He didn't play racial games. And I never heard whites complaining about him either. When you talked to him, he'd steeple his fingers and listen to you. He was a good listener. He would throw some questions at you sometimes."

To the struggling farmers and cattlemen, to the war veterans and the high school boys eager to move beyond the fields or a mechanic's grease pit, Southwire's sprawling plant, clanking machinery, and feeder rail lines had come to symbolize the New South, a place of hope and opportunity the Atlanta newspapers had talked about for half a century. There it sprawled, just south of the downtown, a thriving, homegrown industrial operation competing head-to-head with the smokestacks and the factories of the North.

"Southwire was central to everything down there," remembered Larry White, a Carroll County native who later worked with the SCR group in Asia and Europe. "All my relatives worked for Southwire. If we hadn't, we'd be poor white trash out in the middle of nowhere, living out of double-wides or single-wides. The company gave all of us an economic foundation." If you were willing to work hard and master skills, Richards was as good as his word: you'd move up the ladder, earn a decent living year in, year out without the worry of landowners, droughts, or weevils . . . maybe trade your blue collar for a white one, your rusting Chevy pick-up for a new Ford F-100. You could savor the fact that, after many generations of just getting by, you could provide a future for your children.

"I grew up surrounded by a bunch of cows," remembered Mike Wiggins, today Southwire's executive vice president of human resources. "I remember working in a service station, washing cars, doing things like that. I knew that at Southwire a bunch of people in the community had progressed from operator, to supervisor, to department head. One guy would come into the service station every week to cash his check. He'd show me his profit-sharing projection and say, 'You gotta come over there with us!'

"I'd struggled just to get through school," Wiggins continued, "but I eventually came to work here because I'd seen others grow and profit. My first job, they put me on the third shift, working nights, but the growth was such you knew that if you busted your ass and were reasonably smart, reasonably intelligent, and had a reasonable education, you could advance. One thing was sure: if you wanted responsibility, they'd give you as much as you could handle."

Actually, at times, it was more than Wiggins could handle. "My introduction to supervision?" he added in response to an interviewer's question. "When I was twenty-two or twenty-three years old, I made it to where I was in charge of the copper refinery on the weekend. I'm big stuff. So I'm standing there one morning in front of the casting operator's booth while liquid copper is coming down into these molds. You have to cool the molds before each new batch of liquid copper is poured. You use mold wash: a mixture that looks like flour mixed with water. It keeps the hot copper from sticking. Unfortunately, liquid copper and water don't mix. I'm in charge, but the operator can't see me. He's busy working these joysticks controlling the tilt of the furnace and the flow of the metal, and the spoons that dump liquid copper from one to another into the mold.

"So he signals a worker to pour in the wash. What happens is the water is supposed to evaporate, but it doesn't. He put in too much wash, so when the liquid copper landed on top of it, there's an explosion! Little slivers of liquid copper hit me in the chest! Everywhere it touched, it burned! It burned a hole in my shirt. I was hurting so bad I couldn't stand it, but I didn't want to admit it. I look around and the casting operator, a giant of a guy, is laughing his ass off. So I jump off the platform and run back up to my office. I jerk my shirt off to see how bad I'd been burned. It looked like I'd been hit by a shotgun blast. And these guys are laughing!

"This was a macho, macho place in those days. Guys would play practical jokes that would get you fired in a second today. They'd take a spark plug wire off the lift truck and put it under the driver's seat. Guy gets on it—zap! But like I said, it was also a place where a blue-collar guy could move up."

As Roy Richards envisioned, there were synergies and economies of scale, joint ventures and partnerships to be had, deals a canny man could cut that could speed Southwire's growth while offsetting its alarming lack of capital, the handicap of all privately held enterprises. Some of the projects were modest. For example, the wire and cable division (begun after World War II when Richards could not purchase the aluminum cable he needed to string power lines) supported a truck fleet and a wood products division that manufactured pallets. There was a sawmill, perhaps a nod to Richards's father and his own first job.

Other undertakings were enormous: Jonah deciding to swallow the whale. In 1968, Richards entered into an audacious joint venture with National Steel, a Fortune 500 company many times Southwire's size. Its goal: to construct a high-output aluminum smelter on the Ohio River near Hawesville, Kentucky. In an era before stringent environmental and other restrictions were imposed, such smelters were immensely profitable and affordable only to the largest industrial companies. On the other hand, they were eminently susceptible to market downturns and drops in commodity prices. In bad times, they churned out aluminum nonstop, like the swirling mops Mickey Mouse conjured up and lost control of in the *Sorcerer's Apprentice*.

According to an insider familiar with the deal, Southwire put $1 million of its own money into the $140-million-plus cost of the project. In return, Roy Richards negotiated a 50 percent share of the operation. Additionally, National Steel agreed to guarantee the construction cost. On Wall Street, Richards and National Steel representatives engaged Merrill Lynch's investment bankers to underwrite a $145-million industrial revenue bond. At the time, it was the largest such offering in history.

However, federal law capped such offerings—intended for small businesses—at $5 million. Here Roy Richards proved as adept and persuasive in the corridors of power as he was on the factory floor. He approached Senator Herman Talmadge, whose father, Eugene, was a former Georgia governor and whose uncle was the enormously influential Senate powerbroker Richard B. Russell. Senator Talmadge, who sat on the Finance Committee, agreed to shepherd a bill through the Senate that made a special exception for the Southwire/National Steel offering. "Senator Talmadge created the opening," remembered Jim Richards. "And Dad ran right through it."

Specifically, Talmadge inserted a footnote into the IRB bill, accommodating exceptions to the $5-million cap under certain provisions—among them, job creation. The Kentucky smelter would, in fact, create more than a thousand jobs and spin off a host of smaller industries dependent upon aluminum. It was brilliant strategic move. Like Cofer's SCR mill, it would vault Southwire to the top tier of its industry and drive its dizzying growth and earnings for decades.

The smelter came on line in 1969. A rod mill soon followed, adjacent to the smelter. The mill could produce more than seventeen tons of rod per hour. Excess capacity was sold off, seeding a host of aluminum processing businesses—including the first iteration of aluminum wheels for automobiles—in the surrounding area.

"This transaction was considered by most observers as my father's greatest achievement," said Jim Richards, who'd later become Southwire's co-president. "No individual had ever gone and built a smelter. A smelter was something you had to be an Alcoa or Reynolds to do. That plant generated two-thirds of our earnings from 1967 to 2000, when it was sold for more than $400 million." All off a $1-million investment. As one retired Southwire executive later remarked, "Roy Richards was always brilliant at borrowing money."

A privately held company like Southwire can hold its cards very close to the vest. Richards kept more secrets than most men and was fierce in his determination to protect them. Despite the rousing success of the Hawesville smelter, he fumed for fifteen years over the fact that he had to cede two seats on Southwire's board to National Steel in return for their participation.

Roy Richards, shown here with Roger Schoerner, was a brilliant negotiator when it came to borrowing money, investing, and making deals. In 1968, his $1-million dollar deal with National Steel to build a smelter on the Ohio River in Kentucky yielded him 50 percent ownership of the company, which produced over seventeen tons of aluminum rod per hour.

CHAPTER 13

Alchemists of every description and political persuasion descending on Carrollton, determined to turn copper into gold.

IT'S UNLIKELY THAT PETE COFER SPENT HIS TIME reading Shakespeare. He'd barely gotten past his English Lit classes at Millen High. On the road, his tastes ran to tech reports and paperback thrillers. But he would have certainly grasped the significance of a line from *Two Gentlemen of Verona*, exhorting Valentine, a man who, like Cofer, loved to travel and see the world "to make a virtue of necessity."

Roy Richards was living his life by that dictum. Southwire's aluminum and copper continuous rod capability was developed out of dire necessity: to feed and grow the wire- and cable-making side of the company at a time when it was being starved by monopolistic competitors. Necessity, once embraced, becomes a virtue, with significance far beyond the merely self-sufficient. Word of Pete Cofer's signal breakthrough spread quickly through the industry and then overseas via trade publications, tech reports, trade shows, conferences, word of mouth, and gossip.

Soon, what a newspaper report of the period described as a "constant flood" of neatly dressed businessmen and engineers carrying bulky briefcases was bypassing Atlanta's bristling downtown and making its way to tiny Carrollton in west Georgia. Japanese, Chinese, Taiwanese, Koreans, West Germans, Brazilians, Brits, French, Russians, South Africans. They all came. And later came Kazakhs from Central Asia, Hindus from India, Turks, Egyptians and Indonesians, Bulgarians, Poles, representatives of lesser-developed countries struggling to modernize.

To the locals, these visitors were as exotic as unicorns at first. They began to make appearances at Carrollton motels, shops, and restaurants—and the stories they could tell! Southwire's Japanese agent, Teruma Hamada, for example, had been an officer in the Japanese Imperial Army, among the first of the rescue units to enter Hiroshima after that city was devastated in the summer of 1945. Childless because he feared his exposure to radiation at ground zero would result in deformed offspring, he spent many an afternoon on the patio of his Carrollton motel quietly sipping his favorite Cutty Sark whiskey.

In Atlanta, the upstart media mogul Ted Turner prattled on and on about the importance of "internationalism"—even banning the term "foreign" from CNN broadcasts—but the real internationalism was taking root in Carrollton. Among the pilgrims were executives from Westinghouse Electric, Inspiration Consolidated Copper, and other onetime (or future) competitors, come to observe the rod mill firsthand, gather information for headquarters' reports, make initial inquiries about purchases, time frames, and customer support. They also came to pitch or be pitched by Roy Richards on joint ventures and partnerships. Taken together, alchemists of every description and political persuasion descended on Carrollton determined to figure out how to turn copper into gold.

Pete was there to greet them. Like Richards, here was a man who, in that great American tradition, had completely reinvented himself by dint of enterprise, ingenuity, and hard work. Cofer was anyone's equal—engineer, educator, executive, salesman, raconteur, inventor. He'd been to exotic places and could charm and entertain, spellbind with technical wizardry, answer questions, and offload as much data as anyone could handle, all at his fingertips or in the black notebooks he carried in his left front pocket the way the Communist Chinese carried Mao Zedong's *Little Red Book*.

And sure enough, in the 1970s, SCR copper rod systems became the worldwide standard of reliability and performance, a position they hold to this day. Southwire mills purchased by Furukawa Electric, Hitachi Wire Rod Company, and Mitsubishi Materials Corp. in 1971, for example, were capable of reliably producing twenty-five to forty-eight tons of rod per hour and could be upscaled or downsized, improvements added on seemingly as easily as a pair of trousers stitched by a Tokyo tailor.

Roy Richards's dire necessity had become Southwire's virtue. He understood that marketing the SCR systems, which were originally priced at around $2 million each and soon escalated in cost and complexity, would require top-notch sales, legal, logistics, and support. He needed horsepower to pursue, negotiate, and close deals, assemble the mills, train operators, shepherd the projects as they came on stream, and provide upgrades as well as first-class customer service. The visionary in Richards also saw that the bulk of this untapped business would take place overseas, first in modern, developed economies, but later in Communist-bloc and Third World markets woefully lacking in infrastructure and skilled labor. In these markets, the competition was intense and happily corrupt, business practices were byzantine, and the only law one could reasonably assume to be in effect was Murphy's Law.

To seize this opportunity, Richards knew that Southwire needed men with experience, savvy, discipline, know-how, and stamina to manage such assignments. Pete Cofer was the first and most successful of these. Another was former Marine officer Chap Chandler, who would later run the Hawesville aluminum smelter. Others at that level would have likely been Jim Griffin, Gordon Johnson, and Harlan Carroll, Cofer's close buddy, whose job kept him traveling all over the world procuring copper and aluminum to feed the machines.

Under Cofer (named senior vice president, research and development), SCR Technology Sales became, in effect, a semi-independent subsidiary of Southwire; a fair-haired child that, often to the chagrin of other Southwire executives, was given all necessary leeway to get the job done. This, too, became a virtue. Southwire's wire-making margins remained paper-thin, its sales subject to the vicissitudes of the economy and the housing market; its supply of raw materials (what the military calls the "teeth-to-tail ratio") attenuated.

For years, SCR sales and royalties associated with the purchase of a mill (pegged at $2.20 per ton of manufactured rod) helped support the parent company's bottom line, a fact Cofer took inordinate pride in. On more than one occasion, he felt aggrieved that SCR was not given sufficient credit for its outsized accomplishments. "You bet Pete kept score of our sales," remembered one SCR team member. "I've got a spread sheet from day one through our eightieth sale or so. At one point, the rod mills contributed more than 10 percent of the company's profit." Most importantly, because the mills were sold worldwide, the business had a way of buoying Southwire's financial condition when U.S. markets were weak. SCR made everything about Southwire look better.

Which is to say Cofer was a very competitive individual, at times to the point that he infuriated fellow executives. "A lot of the people were jealous because Pete operated independently," recalled Roy Richards Jr. "He was the only guy at Southwire given a relatively free rein." He wasn't shy about defending his favored status, either. The focus of Cofer's ire was often Jim Griffin, vice president of domestic sales. The two would clash regularly over budgets and such—and Cofer would sometimes come out the worse. "Pete and Mr. Griffin were at an equal level within the hierarchy," remembered Ken Kinard, the SCR team's chief salesman, "but Mr. Griffin was a real fine public speaker. He had all the words and was a very smart man himself. He didn't want any of this SCR stuff sold in the domestic marketplace because it would come back and make his sales job tougher.

"Pete wasn't glib. He didn't give big speeches and use eloquent words. He cussed and was mentally very tough; he could cut your legs out from under you in a heartbeat. Well, Pete would fight Mr. Griffin straight up in front of Mr. Richards. Trying to do his own very tough job. Griffin would go behind Pete's back and have the ear of Mr. Richards. He'd give him all this nice song and dance on 'why we shouldn't be selling SCR systems to our competitors.'"

Roy Richards and Cofer also had their share of head bumps. Pete could be overbearing and obstinate. "Once a week, or at least once a month," remembered Kinard, "Pete would storm into my office and say, 'I just got fired again!' To his credit, Mr. Richards never got mad. He was really good at not getting mad. Pete was a hothead, but Roy never lost faith in him. Never really fired him." Kinard had a similar relationship with Cofer. Admittedly stubborn and hot-tempered, Kinard got fired regularly as clockwork; once for dumping all the papers from Pete's conference table on the floor. Cofer was obsessed with orderliness.

Roy Richards Jr. believes Cofer's importance to his father rendered any disagreements the two may have had meaningless. There are sycophants in every corporation. Jockeying for position and for praise from the boss is an unfortunate part of the corporate mentality. Cofer was the opposite: a truth teller, a rare thing in the executive suite. "Most of the time Pete acted like the soldier that he was, but privately, he'd tell Dad the truth," Roy Richards Jr. remembered. "He was willing to say 'no.' I know Dad appreciated that."

Back in the day, Southwire was run like a military organization, with Roy Richards as commander in chief. Many of its top executives, Richards, Cofer, and Chandler foremost among them, were Marine or Army veterans, a fact that shaped the corporate culture. They, in turn, recruited men very like themselves. Larry White, a Vietnam veteran who saw much action, was a case in point.

Blunt honesty, the willingness to vociferously defend what you think is right, is a venerable Marine Corps tradition. In 1967, General Victor "Brute" Krulak, no doubt one of Cofer's heroes, famously blew his chances of becoming commandant of the corps by speaking hard truths to President Lyndon Johnson about the diminishing prospects of success in the Vietnam War.

At Southwire, overseas travel became necessary and nonstop. Cofer led the charge. According to one admittedly incomplete company account, in the course of his career, Pete traveled to the United Kingdom fifty-three times, Germany thirty-one times, to France and Spain sixteen times, to Japan at least twenty-three times, to Poland eight times, to Bulgaria eleven times, to Iran thirteen times, to Korea six times. He'd also visit mainland China, Taiwan, Vietnam, Singapore, Hong Kong, Thailand, Malaysia, Indonesia, India, Belgium, Sweden, Switzerland, Hungary, Italy, Turkey, Brazil, Peru, Saudi Arabia, the Soviet Union, and Kazakhstan. There were even more trips; these are just the highlights. At one point, Delta's *Sky* magazine showcased Pete as the airline's most frequent flyer.

Milton Berry, Ken Kinard, John Durscher, Dennis Marlow, Peter Ware, Van Wilks, Johannes Riecker, David Barnes, Yves Bonnamour, Bill Duncan, and George Heyl (Morgan Construction), and an expandable cast of players and overseas reps accompanied Cofer, like some Marlboro-smoking Pied Piper, on hundreds of trips extending from weeks to months.

One overseas-based SCR team member remembers that, on the road, Cofer was a being very different from the no-nonsense taskmaster in the home office. "Fun-loving, boisterous, constantly looking to get into new things." Just-as-quickly, this team member, now retired, says, that after seventeen years working and traveling with the man, chunks of Pete Cofer's personality still remained unknowable. Milton Berry noticed a similar opaqueness in his boss.

"Do you feel you really understand Pete?" he was once asked.

"I don't think he ever intended for me to."

To travel so often and so far must inevitably affect you, threaten to leave you adrift like an astronaut unmoored from Earth's gravitational pull. Languages, borders, time zones, people, world views, the blur of hotel rooms and lousy restaurants; one's spouse and children changing, growing up or apart, in the blink of an eye. The ache of the familiar, passing away . . . the dizzy intoxication of new and constant challenges. Exhaustion. Clearly, Pete Cofer the man, separate from the hard-charging, driven engineer, would have been constantly buffeted by such stresses. He would have struggled against them, even unconsciously, dissonance being abhorrent to the human mind.

Pete Cofer (bottom left) would transition from performing his engineering work in the Carrollton plant to traveling to dozens of countries all over the world multiple times over. Delta Air Lines profiled him one year as their most frequent flyer.

What is knowable is that this tension inevitably ate away at Cofer. It made him careless of his health and well-being, and sometimes irascible, trampling the feelings of his wife, children, and colleagues. What is also knowable is that—though cigarettes are the proximate cause—it shortened his life, deprived him of knowing his grandchildren and some of the comforts of domestic life.

To his credit, he pushed back mightily—the man by all reckoning was courageous—achieved much, became a staunch friend and mentor to many within and outside of Southwire. Some of his colleagues and engineers, men not given to flights of emotion, remember him as almost a second father. Pete's daughters not only loved him, but they cherished him and the rare gift of his company.

This is the true measure of the man, not his feats of engineering.

When he wasn't traveling or working long hours at Southwire, Pete was a "hands-on" father. Here, he and Dott admire their one-month-old daughter Amy.

Chapter 14

I was very capable of taking care of the kids. But the minute Pete walked in the door, oh boy, it was "Hut, two, three, four!"

—Dott Cofer

LIKE TENS OF THOUSANDS OF HOMEMAKERS in the 1960s and 1970s whose breadwinning husbands were often on the road, Dott Cofer essentially had to raise her four daughters herself. "I didn't dwell on it," she remembered. "I told myself, 'I'm Pete's wife, the mother of his kids. It's my job.'" In this family, the notion of "duty" was sacrosanct and unbreakable. What was different in the Cofer household were the endless days her husband was away from home—days Dott woke up early in the morning; spent the day surrounded by four hungry, busy, happy, (and sometimes cranky) children; and staggered to bed fourteen hours later. "My mother was always the volunteer who went on every trip, whether it was a swim trip, a basketball trip, a band trip," Amy Cofer remembered. "She was always there; always the one who had everything anyone needed—a bobby pin, a safety pin, a Band-Aid, a rubber band. She was totally involved in our lives, and everybody depended on her."

In essence, Dott functioned as a single mother at a time when most other wives in the neighborhood had a husband who showed up every night for dinner; or an Army wife without the support systems the military is careful to put into place. Dott, an only child, was not close to her mother. Mariah Cofer, her mother-in-law, lived almost one hundred miles away; her two sisters-in-law were scattered, one as far away as St. Louis.

When he was in Carrollton, Cofer left the house before dawn to meet his breakfast club buddies, and he rarely got home before 6:30 p.m. This was an era when husbands fancied themselves kings and lawgivers. Fathers, no matter how far removed from the daily lives of their offspring, imagined themselves drill sergeants, not friends or soul mates. "I was very capable of taking care of the kids," Dott recalled. "But the minute Pete walked in the door, oh boy, it was 'Hut, two, three, four!'"

He was a hands-on father, though not usually in the modern sense of the word. "We got spanked a lot!" remembered youngest daughter, Ann, with a laugh. "Oh, yeah, Daddy wasn't hesitant." It is no stretch to imagine that Cofer's gut instinct was to impose an engineer's structure and efficiency upon the unpredictable and unruly business of marriage, relationship, family . . . existence itself. He'd separate household chores into "men's and women's work." Children, having no rights, had no say in the matter. This was what he knew, what his own father had done. "I'd watch his mother go to the grocery store and come back in carrying bags," Dott recalled. "All the while, his daddy would be sitting on the sofa watching TV. Where do you think Pete got it?"

He'd reengineer everything, even everyday life. "He insisted on paying bills only on the first of the month," Dott remembered. "Even when they were due on the fifteenth."

"Pete, do you expect these companies to change their way of doing business to please you?" she'd plead.

"Yes."

"And that was what he did."

In Carrollton, legend has it that when Amy, Jean, Kay, and Ann were old enough to begin dating, Pete had a pay phone installed in the kitchen of the Highland Avenue house. "That wasn't the case," insisted Dott. What is true is that he would not allow more than one phone on the premises in a house with four chatterbox girls. When his daughters did start attracting beaus, his behavior was in keeping with his personality—quirky. He refused, for example, to learn the names of any would-be suitor until he was convinced the boy's intentions were serious. Daughter Amy described the drill when one of these hapless young men showed up at the Cofer residence:

"The doorbell would ring. We'd hear the arm on his La-Z-Boy click down . . . hear him shuffle to the door, open the door. The boy would say, 'I'm here to pick up Jean or whomever.' Daddy would turn around, with the boy standing in the doorway, and scream down the hall, 'Jean, your Melvin is here!' The bell would ring again, and he would schlep to the door, 'Kay, your Melvin is here!'"

"It's true," Dott insisted. "He called every one of them Melvin."

Beneath Cofer's gruff exterior was, well, a gruff interior. God forbid any of the Melvins dared call after Pete had turned in for the night. This was usually around 9:00 p.m. His daughters recall him leaping out of bed and grabbing the phone.

"May I talk to—"

"Too damn late!"

And then he'd chew the boy out for five minutes.

His daughters remember these outrages with great affection. They insist theirs was a loving father, though one occasionally at war with his own feelings. The truth is, no one teaches men how to be fathers. They either model themselves on their own experience or, in Pete's generation, tough it out, adopting the role of stern authoritarian. Pete tried this approach, but inevitably his humanity and outgoing nature undercut him. Hazel Sprewell, the secretary who probably spent more time with Cofer than anyone outside his family, remembered, "Deep down, Pete was a very softhearted person."

He gave Hazel, for example, permission to arrive and leave work early every day so she could drop off and pick up her young children at school, a privilege typically verboten in the buttoned-down corporate world of the time. Many years later, when Dott Cofer was diagnosed with breast cancer, Pete was literally at a loss. "He wasn't going to take care of me," Dott recalled, "because he didn't know how. That was just not in his nature. But he made sure somebody did. That's a big difference."

When Dott's mother, Clare, developed Alzheimer's disease, it was decided that she had to be relocated from Wesley Woods, an assisted living facility near Decatur, to another facility in Carrollton (Dott's father had since passed away). Struggling, as all children do with such a burden, an emotionally wrought Dott turned to her husband.

"Pete, we have to do something with Mother. I need your help!"

"Of course I'll help."

When the time came, he dropped everything and engineered the move. "It was like a movie production," Dott recalled. "That morning he drove over to Wesley Woods with me." When Dott and Pete went inside, daughter Jean was waiting in the parking lot with the moving van. There was a script to be followed, designed to ease the old woman's stress:

"Mother, we haven't been to the cemetery in a long time," Dott suggested at one point. "Wouldn't you like to visit Daddy in the cemetery?"

"Yes, I'd like to do that."

"We went to the cemetery," Dott remembered. "The minute we left, the movers removed all her furniture, transported it to the nursing home in Carrollton, and set up everything exactly as it was in her room at Wesley Woods.

"After the cemetery, I said, 'Mother, Kay's got a new house. Let's go have lunch with Kay.'"

"Okay, we'll do that."

"We had lunch and then took Mother to the nursing home in Carrollton. She looked around; everything seemed exactly as she had left it. It never dawned on her that she wasn't still in Decatur. She was that bad. Later, when she settled in, I had to take her to the doctor. And she said, 'Oh there's Southwire! I didn't know Southwire had a plant in Decatur!'

"You know, Pete made it all happen."

CHAPTER 15

*Pete would ask you to do something, not knowing what he
wanted done. And when you'd come up with something,
he didn't mind telling you that that wasn't it.*

—HAZEL SPREWELL

AT SOUTHWIRE, HAZEL SPREWELL WAS FOREVER scrambling, filling out pass-
port renewals and visa requests, fielding Pete's static-filled overseas phone calls, and jotting
down notes from his telexes. "The traveling was very, very extensive," she recalled. "He'd
fly to Europe and go to a different company in a different country, one right after another.
He'd stay two or three weeks. When he had really complicated negotiations, he'd stay a
month."

In the run-up to one of these trips, Sprewell had lists of reports, technical materials,
appointments, the precious slide rule, all ready to pack into Cofer's bulging briefcase.
"There was paperwork for each company that he planned to visit overseas," she recalled.
"Goodness, the research and stuff he did! He could never have enough knowledge in whatever subject he was interested in."

Nor enough cigarettes or coffee. His natural hyperactivity was supercharged by
endless caffeine and mellowed by cigarettes.

"When he arrived back from overseas, I had to do as many as ten different trip reports, one on each company he visited," Sprewell remembered. "Then right away, it was
on to new business.

"Pete would call me into his office. 'We need to do so and so. And such and such.'
He always had a list made and called it out to me. I'd write it down or take shorthand.
Then he'd pause and add dramatically, 'But before we do that, I'd like a cup of coffee.'"

Cofer would assure Hazel in no uncertain terms that he despised "put-ons" and
"people with airs." Of course, being Pete, he could tell instantly who these people were.
When it came to his own behavior, no one would ever accuse him of putting on airs. If
anything, the pendulum was likely to swing in the opposite direction. Cussing is embedded
in every leatherneck's DNA. Pete tried to watch his language—he really did, particularly
around Roy Richards—but often, he'd let loose a stream of blue language. Hazel, a church-
goer, dutifully closed her ears and kept working. That didn't stop Pete from shooting her
a baleful glance, complaining, "You don't do nearly enough 'helling' and 'damning!'"

When he was in a foul mood, Sprewell and Ken Kinard (whose office was right next to Cofer's) usually bore the brunt of his ire. "Oh, God, Pete was picky," she recalled. "Mostly I saw him being picky with others more than I did myself. He'd ask you to do something, not knowing what he wanted done. And when you'd come up with something, he didn't mind telling you that that wasn't it!"

On the eve of one trip to China (Pete was filling in for Roy Richards as part of an entourage put together by Georgia governor George Busby), Cofer kept Hazel working very late. It was Christmas Eve, but that didn't register with Pete. "It was the most aggravated I ever got," she said, her old anger converted to laughter. "My children were home waiting on me. My husband was steaming. Not Pete! He had lists of all these provinces and everything else in China and he kept me there all night.

Hazel Sprewell was executive secretary to Pete Cofer for over twenty-five years. There was great rapport and respect between them as they worked many long hours together, with Hazel managing all the details of his office and travel—even on Christmas Eve!

I guess he was trying to learn this stuff for himself, but he wanted me to learn about it too. On Christmas Eve! Oh, I could have killed him!"

Hazel never did. The two, despite the differences in position, were dear friends. Sprewell was one of Cofer's true sounding boards and confidantes (especially in family matters). She too, had had her share of heartbreak. Of course, none of this ever kept Pete from complaining about her, once famously: "Hazel, you're too damned empathetic!"

PART II

A LIFE ON
THE ROAD

Pete (standing, second from left) and Roy Richards (bottom left) complete one of their many international deals for Southwire.

CHAPTER 16

A computer that does not need electricity

—PETE DESCRIBING HIS SLIDE RULE TO A CHINESE CLIENT

⸺⸺

CHINA. PETE COFER'S WORLD WAR II experiences stamped him for the rest of his life. During most of the Cold War, the Soviets were the bogeymen building a vast arsenal of nuclear weapons, expanding their empire, and supporting "brushfire wars" and insurgencies in the Third World. As a young Marine, Cofer witnessed the birth pangs of the other Communist superpower, one that, in many ways, would become the most formidable challenger to ever confront the United States. For nearly fifty years, "Red China" rattled its sabers against Hong Kong and Taiwan, stoked anticapitalist furor in the Third World, funded proxy wars in Korea and Vietnam, and unleashed a cultural revolution so extreme that it threatened to tear *itself* apart.

Neither the Americans nor the Chinese were farsighted enough to recognize that, in the twenty-first century, this struggle would be for economic rather than political hegemony. Or that a visionary reformer like Deng Xiao Ping would prove as adept and unrestrained at capitalism as any of his counterparts in the United States.

Pete Cofer's adult years were defined by jingoism and rabid anticommunism. The "domino theory" posited that Soviet totalitarians would "flip" the nations of the developing world into its columns, leaving the capitalist West as an island surrounded by enemies. As it turned out, the analysts and theoreticians discounted the incompetence and inhumanity of these regimes and the rising tide of nationalism.

The Chinese challenge was more subtle and complex. In the United States, anti-Chinese prejudice ran as far back as the mid-nineteenth century, when coolies were forced to work on railroads and in mines in subhuman conditions. Many Americans, most prominently the newspaper magnate William Randolph Hearst, declared themselves "nativists," and stoked fears of a "Yellow Peril." Waves of Japanese immigrants, the Issei, who arrived in California in the latter 19th century, endured discrimination in schools, the workplace, and elsewhere. In the aftermath of Pearl Harbor, more than 100,000 loyal Japanese American citizens were stripped of their property and rights and forced to spend years in internment camps. During the Korean conflict, "slopes" and "Chicoms" (Chinese Communists) were stereotyped as treacherous, subhuman, mindless, unfeeling. They were not considered individuals, but, rather, alien swarms.

This is the political background against which Southwire and other American corporations were forced to operate during the Cold War. Pete Cofer, despite his World War II experiences, harbored no such prejudices. If anything, he operated in the opposite direction, always seeking the human being behind the politics and propaganda. "Pete always had a special place in his heart for China, and a special interest in the people and culture," recalled Larry White, the SCR team member who crisscrossed Asia with Cofer for seventeen years.

Pete traveled to Taiwan and mainland China at least a dozen times and walked the crowded streets of Hong Kong, Beijing, Shanghai, and a dozen other cities. He endured the lousy hotels, visited crumbling monuments, and rode alongside peasants and business-men on creaking trains running the same schedules they'd had when he was a Marine thirty years before. "I remember times when he could have sent me out with a couple of engineers to visit these factories or handle technical presentations on our own," White added, "but Pete enjoyed it and enjoyed the traveling."

White is a native Georgian who grew up in Carroll County and, like tens of thou-sands of young Southerners before him, joined the Army to improve his lot in life. In one of those unexpected twists of fate, he was assigned to the prestigious Defense Language Institute in Monterey, California, where he proved himself a natural linguist. He studied Chinese but was packed off to Vietnam. In addition to fluent Chinese, White also learned passable Vietnamese and Japanese.

He was hired by Southwire to oversee its office in Taiwan. There, Pete had him prepare a basic English–Chinese dictionary that focused heavily on the technical terms utilized by the wire and cable industry. He also had White translate a number of SCR technical papers and other educational materials he thought would be useful in selling the rod mills. Hundreds of copies of these papers were printed, and they seemed to take on a life of their own. "From 1984 onward," White recalled, "we relied on these Chinese materials. On many occasions when we'd visit a new client, we discovered our material was already there! They'd been cir-culated before we even knew we were going to meet the client. Pete understood the Chinese well, and he knew this would happen. Our good reputation prepared the way for our visits."

The intrigue Cofer had observed in his days as a military courier in China served him well in peacetime. He was quick to put White's linguistic skills to tactical use. As White later explained, "When we started traveling to China in 1982, we didn't know whom to trust. Or who would help or hurt us in negotiations. Pete asked me to sit at the table when we met with clients and agents, and *not say a word in Chinese*. Just take in what was going on. Well, we met with ten or fifteen different parties. Let's just say we learned quite a bit about who was for us and who wanted to take advantage of us."

Competition for new business was intense, as were the hammer-and-tongs negotiations of contracts and deals. By all accounts, Cofer was a superlative negotiator. Recalled one SCR team member, "Pete would give in on something in one sentence of a contract and then take it away somewhere else. An 'exclusivity clause' might be given where Southwire agrees to sell ex-clusively to client 'A' for five years in their market. Then Pete would slip in a 'competing sys-tems' clause elsewhere in the contract allowing Southwire the right to sell to his competitor!"

The team member watched this strategy unfold on more than one occasion. "I once sat dumbfounded as Cofer seemed to be talking a client *out of buying* an SCR. This was in

Taiwan. We'd already sold two systems to the Walsin Lihwa Corp. (a wire manufacturer). The Walsin's contract contained an exclusivity clause specifying that we could not sell to any of its competitors. However, during the negotiations, Pete had dropped in a sentence saying we would not sell to any competitor *unless that competitor was intent on buying a continuous casting system from one of our competitors.*

"Well, Taiwan's Pacific Electric Wire and Cable Company (PEWC) was threatening to purchase a German system even though they preferred Southwire. This should give you an idea of the intrigues involved in some of these negotiations. Keep in mind our contract with Walsin forbade us from selling our mills to Pacific Electric. So Pete went to the chairman of Walsin and told him we'd lose a sale and they'd have a competing system in their backyard if something was not done. The man sat on his hands.

"Then Pete went to PEWC chairman Mr. Sun Tao-tsun and begged him to come to an arrangement with Walsin. Of course, Pete quietly offered him some initiatives that were beneficial to both parties and seemingly disadvantageous to Southwire. Chairman Sun reemphasized his intention to buy the German system if Southwire refused to sell him an SCR. That's where Pete's sentence kicked in! We ended up selling PEWC our rod mill. Over the years, we sold four more SCR systems in Taiwan all because of that one sentence Pete added at the end of Walsin's exclusivity clause."

Neither Roy Richards nor Pete Cofer would ever vouchsafe outright bribery to win a deal, insist SCR team members. In addition to being ethically repugnant, bribery was illegal. The U.S. Foreign Corrupt Practices Act of 1977 prohibited "any person from making use of interstate commerce corruptly, in furtherance of an offer or payment of anything of value . . . to secure any improper advantage in order to obtain or retain business." However, in the cutthroat environment in which they were forced to operate, such practices were commonplace among Southwire competitors, seemingly the price of doing business.

"Our competition had competitive means that we didn't have, that were illegal for a U.S. company," remembered Ken Kinard, who'd become the SCR team's go-to salesman. "The best thing we could do was compensate to a degree by taking our hoped-for customers to the best restaurants, serving them the best wines. I like to think we also had far and away the best product."

Pete Cofer was no altar boy. He was at least capable of spycraft. As one SCR team member who shall remain nameless recalled, "One time, we were having a drink in a hotel bar in Beijing. Pete recognized an ASARCO executive (formerly the American Smelting and Refining Co., a competitor) in the lobby area. The guy had a handful of papers in his hand as he walked over to the reception desk.

"'Stand behind him and listen,' Pete told me."

"Well, this executive gave the clerk at the reception desk directions to fax the papers and then place the fax in his room box. I still remember. It was Room 1022. Then the man left, apparently for dinner. I reported all this to Pete. He grunted and nodded. Every few minutes, I'd walk by reception and check the box. It was empty. When the fax finally appeared, Pete, a very imposing man, casually walked over and spoke to a different receptionist saying, 'I'm Dr. So-and-So in Room 1022 and I need to retrieve my fax.'

"Pete had *his* own room key in his hand, but the receptionist just casually glanced at it without looking at the number. He gave Pete the fax! Back at the bar, we read the papers. After taking notes, I took the fax back and told a receptionist to put it in the box for Room 1022. The message was to ASARCO headquarters, asking permission to make concessions in negotiations with the Chinese client we were also negotiating with. Now that was a useful piece of information."

In China, Cofer's style was always informative, friendly, and low-key. He understood personalities and cultural differences precisely. In Korea, by contrast, it was war; he had to fend off endless bullying attempts to beat him down on price. Each deal was unique and required a particular personal and tactical approach that he'd decide in advance. He kept these strategies, notes, and insights written down in the black notebooks that he kept in his pocket. Selling rod mills to uncertain Chinese bureaucrats and middle managers was an endurance contest. For many of these individuals, the recommendation to make such a purchase was by far the most important decision of their careers. It could make or break a man. Cofer understood and respected that, but one sale could literally take a decade to close.

"Pete was an educator," remembered Larry White. "And our meetings, particularly in mainland China, were often educational. Many of their people didn't have the breadth of technology they needed to make an informed decision. They wanted to be sold on the rod mills, so Pete would sit there and talk SCR all day long. He knew to say things that would generate the right questions so that he could make his point."

During one particularly grueling negotiating session, Cofer's calculator, an antiquated Texas Instruments machine with a mounted printer, malfunctioned. For whatever reason, Pete, who was usually an early adaptor of technology, loved this old calculator. He'd had it for years and had it repaired it numerous times at considerable expense rather than purchase a new one that could perform the same functions more quickly and reliably.

In any event, the chief Chinese negotiator, a man about Pete's age, was sitting across the table from him. He saw Pete was having a problem with the machine and sent an underling to get him another calculator. "Don't bother," said Pete, dropping the unit on the table. He reached into his briefcase and took out the old slide rule that he'd carried since his days at Georgia Tech. To Pete, his slide rule was as familiar and comforting as a nun's rosary beads. "Suddenly, the Chinese negotiator and Pete were best buddies," recalled White, who was sitting alongside Cofer. "The man, also an engineer, had used a slide rule in his years at college and had not done so in years. Like Pete, he found himself dependent on a younger generation's technology and didn't particularly like it. For the next 15 or 20 minutes, they played with the slide rule. Pete even described it to the younger Chinese in the room as a 'computer that did not need electricity.' Soon we were in fruitful negotiations. All because of the damn slide rule."

CHAPTER 17

Best not to smoke Chinese cigarettes.
They stunt your growth!

—DENG XIAO PING TO PETE COFER

CHINA EXERTED A SPECIAL INFLUENCE OVER PETE COFER. He looked at the vast, expansive, and often confounding nation the way a man remembers the first love of his youth. Only in China was he willing to drop his laser-like focus on deals and business. "Of all the countries we traveled to, it was only in China that I saw Pete sightsee," remembered Larry White. "The Chinese loved to show off their national treasures: Mao's birthplace, the Ming Tombs, the Great Wall. We visited so many sites. I began to realize that Pete genuinely loved the culture."

China energized him. Its complex history, culture, politics, and day-to-day life triggered the curiosity, insight, and humor that were essential to his personality. In the early days, when China first opened up to the West, there was plenty to make a Westerner laugh or howl in frustration. "When Pete and I made our first trip in 1982," continued White, "we entered via Shanghai and overnighted at the Peace Hotel before catching a train the next morning. Pete saw there was a Western-style restaurant on the top floor and wanted a final steak dinner before going into the interior of the country. As we entered, there was a sign at the door in English listing the good things about the restaurant: fast service, friendly staff, and clean conditions—eight or ten things. Well, Pete ordered his steak, and when it came, it was burned to a crisp and tough as shoe leather! He ate it as best he could. When we left the restaurant, he stopped by the sign, pointed at it and asked me to take his picture. He said he wanted to remember that the 'sign did not say anything about good food!'"

On another occasion, Cofer and White were returning from visiting a client in Hubei Province in southwest China. "It was the dead of winter, cold as hell," White recalled. "We had to catch a plane back to Beijing, a small, fourteen-passenger prop plane. We got to the airport at 6:00 a.m. for a 7:00 a.m. flight. It was sleeting. They checked us in at the counter and told us to wait. They gave us some hot tea. After a while, we got tired of sitting on cold, hard, wooden chairs and got up for a stroll. We walked to the door, looked outside and saw two Chinese men, one standing on the wing of an airplane with a broom and the other with a long bamboo pole held against his stomach, swishing the pole lightly up and down. The tip of the pole was lightly tapping against the wing. The man with the broom was sweeping up a storm. We watched this in sheer surprise for a few minutes. Pete turned to me and said, 'Chinese de-icing technology?' In shock, I realized that it was our plane the guy was standing on."

On a Taiwan trip to inspect a start-up SCR mill near Taipei that had been purchased by Walsin Lihwa Corp., Pete's hosts, for some inexplicable reason, decided to take him on a tour of a paper recycling plant. The tour had nothing to do with rod-making or wire. The stench was intolerable. Pete stood aghast as rats, bugs, and other organic detritus swirled into the reprocessing vats along with the paper products to be recycled. All through this torment, Cofer smiled and nodded as if impressed by his host's "green" technology. Afterward, standing at a urinal in the plant washroom, Pete turned to Larry White and announced, "I'll never make another spitball as long as I live."

In mainland China, the catastrophic failures of Chairman Mao Zedong's Great Leap Forward (1958) and Cultural Revolution (1966), a violent, decade-long attempt by Mao-inspired Red Guards to purge Chinese society of "capitalist elements" and bourgeois "revisionists," had reduced China to a state of economic, social, and political enfeeblement. Among those purged in the tumult was Mao's old revolutionary compatriot, Deng Xiao Ping. After Mao's death in 1976, Deng, as adept at political intrigue as anyone, returned to prominence. By then, Mao's political henchmen, the so-called "Gang of Four," were in disgrace. Deng outmaneuvered Mao's anointed successor and began to turn the Chinese economy in a radical new direction.

Though Deng would never serve as the Communist Party's general secretary, traditionally the most powerful leadership position, he was a masterful strategist with a clear vision for his nation. Deng had little of the hard-liners' rabid antipathy for the West. The reforms he implemented between 1978 and 1992 put China on the road to a market economy and are in large part responsible for the economic powerhouse China is today.

Pete Cofer, who'd witnessed much of this history, now found himself on the cusp yet again. In the aftermath of President Jimmy Carter's move to establish diplomatic relations with the People's Republic, Deng Xiao Ping toured the United States in January 1979. Among his stops were the Johnson Space Center in Houston—he famously wore a cowboy hat—and Atlanta, where he toured the Coca-Cola Company headquarters and a Ford assembly plant. He was a national sensation. At an official dinner hosted by then-governor George Busby, Deng invited a Georgia delegation to visit Beijing.

Among the notables Busby invited to be part of this delegation was Roy Richards. As it turned out, Richards had other commitments and sent Pete Cofer to represent Southwire. As a young Marine, Cofer encountered Chou En Lai (Zou Enlai), later the People's Republic's first premier. Pete never met Deng Xiao Ping, but he remembered delivering a diplomatic pouch to one of Deng's subordinates. Deng and the brilliant Chou En Lai would later become staunch political allies.

In Beijing, it was Deng's turn to host a formal dinner for the Georgian delegation. The protocol for such affairs can be reduced to very simple terms: sit around and mimic what the host does. During the course of a very long dinner, the chain-smoking Pete was dying for a cigarette. He didn't dare smoke, because no one else had done. He sat there getting more and more antsy. One SCR veteran picked up the story:

Finally, Deng himself lit up. Immediately, so did Pete—that was all the signal he needed. No one else at the table was smoking; just the two of them puffing away like kids in a schoolyard. After the dinner, Deng stood at the door to shake hands as the guests filed out. When the six-foot-four Pete came up to shake the hand of his five-foot-tall host, Deng looked up and asked what brand Pete smoked. Pete took out a pack of Marlboros and offered him one. Deng took out a pack of Chinese smokes (most likely Five Star brand), hesitated, but did not return the offer. Grinning, he warned Pete, 'Best not to smoke Chinese cigarettes. They stunt growth!' They both laughed.

The seeds Cofer sowed in China continued to bear fruit, a harvest that contributes to Southwire revenues to this day. Between 1975 and 2012, the SCR teams sold seventeen copper rod mills to the People's Republic of China; four of these were joint ventures brokered by the Taiwanese. They, in turn, purchased five SCR and one aluminum rod mill. If anything, these efforts contributed in a small way to the rapprochement that continues between the two old antagonists.

CHAPTER 18

Everything we had set out to do that week was in that satchel.
We'd be made or broken by what was in that satchel. And Pete
was lugging that thing through Narita Airport in the middle
of the night with a cigarette dangling from his lip.

—ROY RICHARDS JR.
ON TRAVELS WITH PETE

JAPAN. WHEN PETE COFER BEGAN TRAVELING TO JAPAN in the 1970s, the island nation had long since put the ravages of World War II behind. The Land of the Rising Sun was well on its way to becoming the industrial powerhouse the world would soon come to know as "Japan Inc." American college students were driving Hondas and Toyotas, teens were toting Sony Walkmans, and Japan was dominating entire American markets. The powerful pre–World War II financial and industrial conglomerates known as zaibatsu had evolved into modern multinationals like Mitsubishi, Sumitomo, and one of Southwire's best clients, Furukawa Electric.

Electricity was the lifeblood of Japanese expansion, transmitted via arterial systems of cable and wire, no different from any of the scores of nations invested in Southwire rod mills. The Japanese were robust customers and shrewd businessmen, not only buying mills for domestic use but also participating in numerous joint ventures in less-developed countries like Malaysia and Vietnam. According to records maintained by Southwire's SCR group, Cofer visited Japan as many as fifty-three times (some of these no doubt part of more extensive Asian trips). One SCR engineer remembered traveling to Tokyo at least twenty times. Roy Richards Jr., then a young man, has a "strong memory" of one business trip to Japan with Pete. It captures the man as precisely as if he were preserved in amber:

"I flew to Japan with him to call on Furukawa, quite a long way from Carrollton, Georgia. (At the time, Southwire was involved in a joint venture with Furukawa to manufacture medium voltage cable in the United States) We flew fourteen hours and arrived at Narita Airport at 3:00 a.m. I remember getting off the plane, walking through the terminal and down this very, very long corridor. The airport was nearly vacant, save for the arriving passengers from our plane. Pete had on his beige overcoat, his suit and tie. Everyone wore a suit and tie in those days. His eyeglass frames were transparent, a beige color that for some reason appealed to him, maybe something from the 1950s.

"In any event, here's this tall, stiff, lumbering giant of a man carrying a black satchel so heavy he had to lean sideways to counterbalance its weight. Everything we had set out to do that week was in that satchel. We would be made or broken by what was in that satchel. And Pete was lugging that thing through the airport in the middle of the night with a cigarette dangling from his lip. That's the way it all got done. Long hours, lots of paper and analysis. Tedious negotiations."

According to Milton Berry, the key to successful dealing with the Japanese "was your creditability and your merit, which in Pete Cofer's case was wonderful. The Japanese mentality and the mentality of Southerners," Berry added, "is very similar. A man's word is his bond. Once you establish trust, you've got it made as far as doing business with them." Trust, said Berry, was also built away from the negotiating table, through friendships and lasting relationships cemented over golf games, long dinners, and flasks, called "tokkuri," of warm sake. (Or more to Cofer's taste, Jack Daniels and, on the rare occasions he could get it, Lem Motlow's Tennessee Sour Mash Whiskey.)

"Pete loved his Jack Daniels," remembered Larry White, who traveled regularly to Tokyo. "He'd have a couple of drinks and no more. In all our years together, I never saw Pete drunk . . . In any event, it was my job to bring along a bottle of Jack from the duty-free shop when I joined him from wherever he was coming from. On one trip, we were supposed to travel for two weeks together, but customs would only allow one bottle of whiskey per person. I decided to pull a fast one on Pete. On the plane, I purchased a mini-bottle of Jack Daniels. When I next talked to Pete, I told him I could only get a hold of one bottle for our two-week trip, so we needed to drink sparingly. He agreed. Well, after three days of travel and presentations, we return to our hotel one night tired and ready.

"'Break out the Jack!' Pete exclaimed.

"'Sure thing.'

"I went to my room and got my big bottle and the mini-bottle. When I got to Pete's door, I hid the big bottle outside and went into his room with the mini. There was Pete sitting, reading his spreadsheets with a cigarette in his mouth. When he looked up and saw me carrying the mini-bottle, his mouth dropped and the cigarette fell from his lips. He recovered quickly, reached to take the mini-bottle from my hands and, without blinking an eye, said,

"'Where's yours?'"

Of course, Cofer was usually the guy playing the tricks and unleashing barrages of clever and not-so-clever quips, to the point that SCR team members actually began to look forward to the lame jokes and wisecracks of which he seemed to have an endless supply.

"I'd walk up to his office," remembered Milton Berry, and he'd say, 'Come on in, Ace!'

"And I'd say, 'How do you spell that?'

"'A, double S!'

"That was Pete."

When in Tokyo, Cofer insisted on staying at the New Otani, a pleasant and comfortable hotel near the Akasaka Palace a few miles from the hustle and bustle of the Ginza shopping and tourism district. Behind the New Otani was a private, fenced-in garden with a restaurant Pete christened the "Garden Barbecue." The style of cooking was what Japanese call *teppanyaki*—food cooked on a big iron griddle in front of the customers. The chef, Mrs. Watanabe, who stood all of four foot ten, worked there for years and years. Pete absolutely loved this restaurant and would often joke playfully with Mrs. Watanabe, using Hamada ("Hamada-san") as an interpreter. (In Japan, the suffix *san* is an honorific attached to a last name) The day eventually came when it was time for Mrs. Watanabe to retire. Pete was distraught. He was at a loss without her grilled steak and shrimp, forced to negotiate his way in the alien world of *yakisoba* (fried noodles) or *okonomiyaki* (stuffed pancakes), and worse, much worse.

From that moment on, whenever Pete arrived in Tokyo, Hamada or Larry White would ask the inevitable question and get the predictable answer:

"Pete, where do you want to eat? How about the Garden Barbecue?"

"No, no, it's not the same," he'd say mournfully.

This went on for months and months, remembered White. A day came when Cofer was scheduled to arrive in Tokyo on November 3, his birthday. Hamada knew this and had an idea. He drove over to Mrs. Watanabe's house. When she answered the door, he told her that Cofer-san was due in town. Would she be willing to do a "special cooky" for him? Hamada-san, well-connected and formidable in his own right, then went to the New Otani management and wangled permission for Mrs. Watanabe to come back to work for one day.

Pete checked in at the hotel. Around dinner time, Hamada and Larry White came by.

"I'm starved," Pete said. "Let's go eat."

"How about the Garden Barbecue?" said Hamada.

"No, you know I can't go there anymore"

Hamada turned to White. "What do you say Larry? How about the Garden Barbecue?"

"Yeah I could go there."

"No way," Cofer insisted.

"Come on!"

Sure enough, after a few more go-rounds, Hamada and White, neither very tall, marched their hulking boss to the garden gate. When he walked through the entrance, Pete spied Mrs. Watanabe working her magic at the grill.

"A big old smile you couldn't believe came over Pete's face," recalled White. "She came out from behind the counter, and he gave her the biggest hug. We snapped a bunch of pictures. Here's this four-foot-ten woman next to six-foot-four Pete. I swear you could see tears in his eyes. He was that happy."

On other occasions, things did not work out as swimmingly. On the road in Japan and elsewhere, Cofer prided himself on being able to eat anything, particularly when his host was a client or potential customer. Losing face or embarrassing someone through a cultural faux pas was a risk he would never take. One time, he arrived at the New Otani to meet a delegation of Furukawa Electric executives. As is the custom, his hosts chose the menu, which was unusually exhaustive. Amidst many courses and much toasting, an unknown delicacy arrived at Pete's table. Pete blinked, stared uncomprehendingly at it. Next to him, SCR engineer Jim Shadinger was also looking a little pale. Pete looked at the cup in front of him more closely, making sure none of the Japanese were watching. It had the appearance of chocolate pudding, but the texture was all wrong. According to Shadinger, "a lot like chocolate pudding with yellow mucus in it."

Years later Shadinger recalled, "I tried tasting a little bit. Not good."

At the time, Shadinger turned to Hamada, hoping for an explanation. Hamada, typically dour, mumbled a few guttural syllables that made things dramatically worse for the Americans.

"We never did get the translation straight," said Shadinger in 2011, "but either way, not good. I understood from Hamada, "bowels of sea rats," or "balls of sea rats."

As Shadinger watched in horror, Cofer plowed ahead, grimacing and swallowing the substance down. "This was the only time," Shadinger remembered with a laugh, "I'd ever seen where Pete looked like he wasn't going to be able to handle it."

More than likely, the dish was *uni*, a seasonal delicacy much prized in Japan. As it turns out, Hamada's translation, though literal, was not far off. "Sea rat" is a spiny undersea creature much like an urchin. Its gonads are served as sushi, and, of course, eaten raw.

Hamada and Cofer were business associates *and* good friends, despite being worlds apart in culture and outlook. The possibility of such a friendship is key to understanding the complex human being that was Pete Cofer, and the siren song, that seductive array of possibilities, risks and chance encounters that are part and parcel of a life lived on the road.

Hamada was of Cofer's generation, a traditional, straight-laced Japanese businessman. Though soft-spoken and polite, he would not hesitate to express his point of view—all the way up to Roy Richards and his sons—when he disagreed with a Southwire approach, policy, strategy, or commitment. He was politically conservative and active in an organization that attempted to locate and repatriate World War II Imperial Japanese Army soldiers still hiding in the Pacific jungles.

When he learned of one such half-starved veteran discovered in the Philippines, Hamada told Cofer he wanted to find a way to honor the man. As Cofer got to know him better, he discovered that Hamada, who favored Cutty Sark scotch as much as Pete loved Jack Daniels, had served as an officer in the Japanese Imperial Army. In fact, Major Hamada was part of the rescue mission that was sent into Hiroshima after the atomic bomb was dropped in August 1945. Hamada rarely mentioned his wartime experiences. But one time, when he was in his cups, he described the horror and confusion he felt not knowing what was happening. He said he couldn't believe that such devastation could be caused by a single bomb.

Like many successful Japanese businessmen, Hamada was an avid golfer and quite proud of his membership in an elite golf club. In Japan, golf practically rivals Shintoism as a national religion. As in the United States, the pristine, scissor-clipped greens of the best clubs are fertile soil for planting the seeds of friendship and business. "There is something about a conference table that brings out the worst in people," insisted Ken Kinard. "On a golf course, Pete could do things he could never get away with around a negotiating table." Sometimes, completely unexpected things.

"One time, I remember Pete teeing off at this very exclusive course with a group of top-level Hitachi executives," Kinard continued. "He placed his ball in front of the tee markers. This is a 'no-no.' You can't do it. The markers are there as a boundary on the tee box. Well, Pete hit a good shot, but it was an illegal shot. However, the rules of play also say that the people you're playing with can allow an exception.

"You make a mistake," one of the Japanese said delicately.

"Pete was always quick with his brain," Kinard continued, laughing at the memory. "He went back and picked up the tee markers and moved them in front of where he teed!

"The Japanese loved it."

On another hole, Pete suggested to his hosts that he would hit their tee shot and they would hit his. They nodded in agreement.

"Hit first," Cofer insisted politely.

"One of the Japanese stepped up and hit a reasonable drive," said Kinard. "That's the shot Pete would play second. Now it was Pete's turn to drive *his* shot. He walks up to the tee and intentionally hits the ball into the lake!

"This is comical in a minor sense," Kinard added, "but it's very intellectual, and it got right to them. People in every country, especially Japan, want to examine your personal character. It's not only 'how good is your system, what's your price, and what's your delivery?' It's 'what are you made of . . . can we do business with this guy?'

"This is where Pete was at his best."

Despite his buttoned-down persona, Hamada enjoyed his share of off-color jokes and a daily round of Cutty Sark scotch. At one point, Hamada introduced Cofer, Kinard, White, and other Southwire folks to a bar he favored near the New Otani Hotel, a place where few Western tourists ever darkened the door, no doubt part of its appeal. The bar became so popular that Hamada affixed a plaque outside identifying the establishment as "Southwire Night Office."

"This is where the real negotiations took place," remembered Ken Kinard. "Not officially, but where many of the deals were done." The bar was run by two ancient crones who, with Hamada or Larry White interpreting, told the raunchiest jokes. "Pete would laugh and laugh and fire jokes right back at them," recalled White. "He took real joy in this kind of stuff."

In the mid-1980s, golfing great Jack Nicholas designed a course outside Tokyo, one of hundreds he's associated with in every corner of the globe. This one, part of the Kazusa

Monarch Country Club, is about an hour's drive from the center city and had quite a party reputation among Japanese and Westerners with the juice to play there. On one visit to Kazusa, Cofer encountered a senior executive with the rival British Insulated Callender's Cable (BICC Ltd.) at the club. Much drinking ensued, according to an eyewitness, and at one point, the man fell dead asleep.

Ever ready for a prank, Pete either convinced or bribed the staff of the Kazusa Monarch to go through the building and set all the clocks ten hours ahead. The executive woke up, disoriented and hung over, many hours later. He glanced at the clock and, to his horror, realized he'd missed an entire day's meetings and negotiations! This was still another side of Pete Cofer, a man willing—hell, *happy* to expend time and energy playing a trick he wouldn't get to see pay off.

Cofer pulled a variation of that same prank at a crowded New Year's Eve party in Carrollton, somehow convincing his hosts to tip the blaring television on its side. When a partygoer, many sheets to the wind, staggered in to watch Guy Lombardo and his Royal Canadians usher in the New Year, Pete had convinced all the other guests not to let on that anything was amiss.

In the summer of 1985, Cofer and White, who'd replaced an ailing Hamada, traveled to the Yazaki Electric Wire Company. It was a visit that demanded all of Cofer's skill and diplomacy. On one level, he intended to discuss terminating a floundering Southwire/Yazaki joint venture manufacturing Triple E aluminum alloy wire, a product Yazaki was hoping to add to its automotive products line. At the time, the Yazaki founder had passed on, and his sons, much like Jim and Roy Richards Jr., were running an international corporation begun by an entrepreneurial father.

The Yazaki brothers wanted to express their appreciation for Southwire's sticking with the unprofitable venture for many years. At the same time, they were focused on aggressive expansion: their goal was to become the world's largest automobile harness manufacturer. To do that, they felt they needed to be assured of Southwire's support. Pete Cofer, they believed, would be key to winning the Richards brothers over. Specifically, they were planning to build a factory in northern Mexico (Arnecom) and needed a dependable supply of copper wire. They also knew that Southwire maintained a fleet of trucks that delivered nationwide, and they were subtly feeling Cofer out about using the fleet to deliver their harness wiring from Mexico to customers like Daimler-Chrysler, Ford, GM, and a handful of Japanese automakers then operating in the United States.

At the time of Cofer's visit, they did not ask for any commitments. Japanese businessmen, unlike their Korean counterparts, are subtle, rather than blunt or direct. In the course of these discussions, the Yazakis invited Cofer and Larry White to Numazu to tour one of their showcase plants. Numazu is a port city on the picturesque Izu peninsula, approximately 80 miles west of Tokyo. Cofer and White were invited to stay at the Yazaki guesthouse, a signal honor. All major Japanese corporations seem to maintain a number of these showcase villas, typically of traditional design, often surrounded by exquisite gardens, ponds, and manmade waterfalls, encircled by high walls. Within are formal dining rooms with low tables, tatami mats, and cushions on the floor, many bedrooms, steam rooms, traditional baths, sitting rooms, a bar, and so on, all furnished with exquisite wall paintings, silk tapestries, bronzes, porcelain vases, fresh flowers.

At dinner, Pete somehow folded and bent his elongated frame to take his place on the cushions around the low table. The meal ran more than two hours, and always with much drinking and course after course of exotic delicacies. The only chance he had to get up and stretch his legs, Larry White remembered, was when a minor temblor shook the villa halfway through the meal.

Beautiful geishas, most likely arrived from Kyoto the ancient capital city, provided entertainment. Dressed in their patterned silk kimonos and *obi* (the wide, belt-like sash worn over a kimono), the young women danced, sang, and played music on the three-string lute known as the *shamisen*. Aware Cofer was the guest of honor, they went out of their way to lavish their attention on him.

The rest of the evening, White recalled, was much less enjoyable. Cofer's room was furnished with tatami (thick, woven straw mats) for a bed, and a wooden pillow, pure torment for Pete's creaky, middle-aged frame. He wouldn't think of insulting his hosts by mentioning this discomfort and pleading for Western-style bedding. Instead, he unpacked all the clothing from his suitcase, stuffed some socks into one of his dress shirts, and then buttoned up the shirt. A makeshift pillow. When morning finally arrived, Cofer, always ready with a wisecrack, groaned to White, "Desperation is the true mother of invention."

75

In Carrollton, a desperately ill Roy Richards was fighting a losing battle against bone cancer. He passed away in June 1985. His was a devastating loss, both to his family and his company, which had begun to right itself after wobbling mightily amidst the high interest rates and inflationary environment of the Jimmy Carter years. Control of Southwire passed to Roy Jr. and Jim Richards who, for a time, served as co-presidents. Both were in their early twenties and inexperienced.

The Yasaki-Southwire venture did not come to fruition. Southwire's aggressive posture was changing dramatically, and the Richards brothers' focus was necessarily elsewhere: on overhead and debt reduction. Southwire's trucking division and a number of other units were sold off or shut down as part of a cost-cutting and consolidation cycle they were forced to implement. The Yazaki brothers did build plants in Mexico, Nicaragua, and elsewhere. They remain highly successful today.

CHAPTER 19

Delays. Flight cancellations. Hotel bookings not working out.
To Pete, it was just another thing along the way.

—JIM SHADINGER

PETE COFER TRAVELED IN AN ERA WHERE THERE were fewer direct international flights; he traveled to parts of the world where connections and layovers were unpredictable and routinely canceled; where missed trains, irascible border guards and customs agents—no matter how much goodwill was doled out—could keep him trapped in some sweltering or festering limbo for days on end. Like a modern Odysseus with a clip-on tie, he lived by his wits, never knowing whether he'd be greeted by the siren song of willing customers or gutted in the ravenous jaws of his competitors.

Cofer's odyssey carried him to India a number of times. In 1989, he arrived in Mumbai—one of the world's most intriguing and confounding cities—to begin a round of negotiations with representatives of Hindustan Copper, Southwire's first customer on the subcontinent. Cofer checked in at the Mumbai Oberoi Hotel, one of the city's great luxury hotels, still discomfited from the squalor and smells along the hour-long drive from the airport. Over the next few days, Pete and engineer Jim Shadinger toured the site of the proposed rod mill—an industrial corridor in Taloja across the Vashi Bridge from Mumbai—and then flew with a group of Hindustan reps to the company's Calcutta headquarters. When those meetings ended, they were off to New Delhi.

"We arrived at the Calcutta airport (formerly 'Dum-Dum Airport') and something had happened with our connecting flight," recalled Shadinger. "We were forced to reschedule. We make our way to the ticketing counter where the airline agent is sitting behind a sheet of glass with a circular hole for us to speak through. Don't forget, Pete is a big man. As tall as he was, Pete's head did not match up with the hole in the glass. Pete's up here, and the guy's down there. Anyway, Pete leans forward to try to communicate with him better and see the flight schedule at the same time.

"*Bang!*

"Pete's head hits the glass. It shatters! I assume it was not safety glass or the kind of plate glass that you'd find in the States. A falling shard hits Pete's hand, which is resting on the top surface of the counter. Like a guillotine. Jeez, Pete is really bleeding! The Indians panic and call some kind of first aid person. He arrives and takes Pete down the way to a medical station. The conditions in there are really filthy. They put something on the cut, and the bleeding begins to slow down. They wrap him up and send him on his way with a handful of bandages.

"The whole time, Pete is making jokes, saying, 'It's okay. I'm okay.'

"They're all afraid he's going to sue them or something. Not Pete. He had no concerns about that. To him, it was just another thing along the way. On our next few stops, everyone is saying, 'Mr. Cofer, why is your hand bandaged? Do you need to go to the doctor?' Never bothered him. If anything, he enjoyed telling the story. Pete seemed to savor the challenges that would come up on a trip. Delays. Flight cancellations. Hotel bookings not working out. In those days, we didn't have the computer capability to check ahead like we do now, so all of this was much more of a problem. Not to Pete. To Pete, it was just part of the job.

India was not Japan with its Kobe steaks or China with its varied and intriguing cuisine. Cofer, practically an omnivore, hated Indian food. He hated the curries and spicy biryanis that are a staple in that part of the world. Here was a man who loved a good steak and found himself in a country where cows walked the streets, sacred and untouchable, while he, stomach rumbling, had to hunt for something, anything, he could eat.

Culture shock cuts both ways. (Mexicans, for instance, complain of the gastrointestinal distress Americans call "Montezuma's Revenge" when they visit the United States.) Years after Pete visited India, a group of Indian engineers arrived in Carrollton for training on an SCR mill. They strolled around the town, as tourists everywhere are wont to do. At one point, one of them pointed in horror at sign prominently displayed in the window of a supermarket: "Winn-Dixie: The Beef People."

In South Korea, Cofer was forced to negotiate with the tough, unyielding bureaucrats who bluffed and feinted, blustered, bullied, and sang the competition's praises to his face. The Indians had their own torturous methods to wring concessions out of a negotiation—death by a thousand snubs and indignities. Jim Shadinger recalled:

> Pete could go as long as anybody wanted to meet or negotiate. When we got to India, he took me aside and explained their tactics: 'We'll arrive at their office at the appointed time, but they will not meet with us. No, they'll put us in some crowded, hot, little room and make us wait. And wait. This is how they demonstrate they're in charge. You've got to learn to adjust. Don't let it get to you.'

Sure enough, when the Hindustan executives finally appeared, the first thing they did was insist that Southwire's Indian agent, Ram Gupta, be excluded from the discussions. They said Gupta had to be eliminated for competitive reasons because he ran his own wire business, Delta Wire. Then they stuck Cofer, Shadinger, and Morgan Construction Company representative George Heyl in a room until their heels were thoroughly cooled. When the negotiations began, the Indians shuttled in and out of the conference room like a tag team determined to wear the opposing squad down. "If it bothered Pete, he never showed it," remembered Shadinger.

Hindustan is a quasi-governmental operation, and given the glacial pace and density of Indian bureaucracy, it would require many more trips and many more such workouts to close a deal. Fifteen more years, to be precise. And still more years before the Southwire rod mill actually came on-stream. Even after a decade's worth of delays, the torture didn't end. In 2011, Pete Cofer had long passed away and Shadinger, nearing retirement, was still fielding weekly, "even daily," queries, complaints, and questions from Hindustan about the mill's operation.

If he had to be direct to make a point, Cofer was ready and willing, though he preferred to leaven in-your-face bluntness with humor and rapier wit where he could. On one trip to Spain, Cofer and Ken Kinard arrived in Madrid to meet with representatives of the Rio Tinto Group, a multinational mining consortium. The two made their way to their hotel, worn out after a long flight. At the front desk, Pete pulled a telex from his briefcase that confirmed their reservations. Again, this was an era where there were no cell phones, no e-mail confirmations, and certainly no computers. At the time, Spain was a fascist country, very much under the heavy hand of General Francisco Franco's Falangist party.

"We have no rooms for you," the clerk at the front desk announced archly.
Cofer nodded and considered his options. "Tell me," he said after a moment. "Would you have a room if Generalissimo Franco was arriving?"

"But of course!" the man shot back.

"Well he ain't coming. I'll take his room!"

Rather than argue, the guy behind the desk laughed and handed Pete the room keys. He might as well have whispered, "*!No mas!*

Rarely would anyone come out on top in an exchange with Pete. Repartee and verbal sparring were a vital part of his world, his element, the ultimate stage of an evolution that began all the way back in Millen, Georgia, when he was a teen wisecracking about violations of his "Fourth Amendment protections against illegal search and seizure" to a deputy sheriff looking to write him a traffic ticket.

Among the many hats he wore, Cofer served as a kind of executive bill collector with recalcitrant customers, and there were many. Again, he preferred wit and humor to threats and bluster. As mentioned, Southwire had a royalty system in place on the SCR mills. In simple terms, fees were assessed according to each mill's annual output of copper rod. These royalties accrued at the rate of $2.20 a ton over a fifteen-year term. Considering that a rod mill could be configured to produce hundreds of thousands of metric tons per year, SCR royalties became a very significant part of the company's profit picture.

The practically indestructible mills ran year after year, even as the connection between Southwire and some of its customers grew as tenuous as a thirty-gauge strand of wire. Some clients made it a point of honor to try to avoid making those last few royalty payments. Others whined and wheedled like a New Yorker in a rent-controlled apartment falling behind on their rent. In 1977, Southwire had sold a rod mill to Italian industrialist Carlo Colombo. Installed in the town of Pizzighettone, southeast of Milan, the plant operated as a subsidiary, *Colata Continua Italiana* (CCI), under Colombo's elder son, Giorgio. Over the years, its output increased from 140,000 metric tons per year to 240,000 tons.

Carlo Colombo was a self-made man, and who, like many such men, insisted on seeing the world through his own lens. At the time, Italy was paralyzed by a series of high-profile kidnappings, targeting politicians and the ultra rich. In 1978, the extreme left-wing terrorist group *Brigati Rosse* kidnapped and murdered former Italian prime minister Aldo Moro and five of his bodyguards. Those who could afford to do so spent much of their time outside the country. The Duke of Milan, Uberto Visconti di Modrone, for example, purchased a cattle ranch about an hour south of Atlanta to escape the predators. John Paul Getty III, grandson of billionaire J. Paul Getty, was not so lucky. He was kidnapped in 1973 and held for ransom. Only when his kidnappers delivered his severed ear to his father was the ransom forthcoming.

Carlo Colombo was not spared these outrages. According to numerous reputable sources and reports, Maurizio Colombo, Carlo's youngest son, had been taken and held for ransom. (As with Getty, the rumors suggest the boy's finger had to be delivered before the elder Colombo paid up.) When Pete Cofer arrived in Milan, Giorgio Colombo, Maurizio's older sibling, was in no mood for small talk. He arrived from Pizzighettone in a black, armored limousine with a contingent of bodyguards. It was not exactly the right atmosphere for Pete to try his hand at debt collection. After dinner, sitting in his armored limo, Colombo came straight to the point.

"Tell me Pete: why are you here?"

"To collect our royalties."

"I can't pay! I can't pay you!"

"I want our damn money!" Cofer shot back. "I know you have it."

Ken Kinard winced as the argument intensified and wondered what Pete's next move would be. The royalties ran hundreds of thousands of dollars.

"*Disgraziato*, what if I *won't* pay you!" Colombo shouted.

Cofer turned to face him. He waited a long moment, calm as could be, then replied, "I'll roll your goddamn windows down!"

Giorgio blinked and then laughed. His anger melted. Pete Cofer was no rascal or rogue. Of course, the Italian knew that. No doubt much of his anger was feigned, a negotiating tool. He agreed to settle up.

Of course, Giorgio had the last laugh. He never mentioned to Pete that, broke as he was, he'd just purchased a $12-million oceangoing yacht.

CHAPTER 20

We are happy that a person like you has been born to the world, and we celebrate your birthday today.

—GENNADY AGUZHEN
GENERAL DIRECTOR OF ARTYOMOVSK NON-FERROUS METAL WORKS, TO PETE COFER

WHEN THE FIRST WARM BREEZES OF *PERESTROIKA* began to blow in the Soviet Union in the mid-1980s, Southwire was already on the march. Cofer and the SCR team had made contact with Ukrainian-born Dr. Diamar Belij, who at the time was chief metallurgist in the All-Union Institute of Cable Industry in Moscow. Belij would later work at the Elkat plant in Moscow where the first SCR mill in the Soviet Union came online. Today, Belij is a consultant at Zao Cabix Ltd. in Moscow.

That initial contact was the beginning of a friendship between the Soviet technocrat and Southwire that would span more than three decades. Upon the arrival of the Carrollton contingent in Moscow, Belij—a gregarious bear of a man, much like Pete—would greet each visitor with a crushing hug. His English, however, was practically nonexistent, and Belij was rarely without his attractive and highly capable translator, Tatiana "Tanya" Golubeva, who would eventually displace the official "minder" assigned to the Southwire contingent.

As the Cold War was thawing, Cofer and his team were closing their first deal (a joint venture with the Finnish firm Nokia) to build a high output rod mill—Elkat—outside Moscow. There would be other SCR contracts with the Russians and their former satellites in the years ahead: Uzkabel in Tashkent, Uzbekistan; Kazkat in Kazakhstan; Artyomovsk Non-Ferrous Metal in the Ukraine; Transkat, Novgorodsky Metallurgichsky and Zoa Kyshtym Electrolytic Copper in Russia. Each deal was fraught with stubborn, often intense negotiations—Pete and his slide rule at the center of the scrum. Southwire's steady breakthroughs paralleled what was unfolding in the political, national, and international arena in Eastern Europe and Central Asia. What struck the Soviets—as it had struck customers everywhere—was Cofer's honesty and his dogged attention to detail. "If a customer asked questions by fax, we knew that he gets *[sic]* the answer the next morning," Tanya recalled years later. "It was his rule—to give an answer without delay, however ever busy he might be. Due to eight-hour time difference between the United States and Russia, we saw his fax messages in the morning, on entering our office. Today, we keep contact with some customers who are still in business, and they all remember how impressed they have been at Pete's extensive knowledge."

Cofer had an uncanny ability to read his customers' professional needs and wants, and, oftentimes, their human needs and unspoken yearnings. In 1992, a delegation arrived in Carrollton from Kazakhstan, the former Soviet Central Asian Republic. The Central Asian Republics—Kazakhstan, Tajikistan, Kyrgyzstan, Turkmenistan and Uzbekistan—were often treated as step sisters by the Russian Soviets who, for example, designated Kazakhstan the site of their nuclear weapons testing and storage.

Among the visitors were Chief Engineer Bulat Abdrakhmanov; Tulegen Abdrakhmanov, chairman of the board of Kazkat Joint Venture; Jury Kartsev, director of the Zhezkazgan copper smelter; and M. Madenov, deputy director of capital construction on the project. The Iron Curtain had already fallen, but this was the first time any of these men had been outside the Soviet Union. As Bulat Abdrakhmanov recalled in 2011, "We looked around with eyes wide open and absorbed all new impressions. I think Mr. Pete Cofer understood our condition."

Southwire arranged for Abdrakhmanov's delegation to fly by private jet for a tour of the smelter and aluminum rod plant in Hawesville, Kentucky. And then Pete Cofer began to work his magic. What follows are Bulat's verbatim impressions of that trip translated from the Russian. His own words are more telling than any paraphrase:

> After the plant tour, we had some time left before departure and were able to see the sights of the great city of New York. We have passed on the city center, visited the UN building, and came to the observation deck one of the towers of the World Trade Center. It seems incredible now, after we all went through the terrible catastrophe of the 'black day'—September 11, 2001. But surprises for us continued. It turned out that our plane is heading to the south of the United States, to Orlando. It was unexpected that Mr. Cofer himself met our group by the gangway of the plane and laid the red carpet on the ground as for the most honored guests!
>
> Pete was a man with a wonderful sense of humor; we have seen this time and again. He was driving himself a minivan from Carrollton to Orlando. In our country, the executive of his level would have traveled in the company limousine with a personal chauffeur . . . Cofer has been walking with us in the Disney World with pleasure; we all went on the rides, eat ice cream, took pictures, watched the parade of Disney heroes. As if we were in a fairy tale and felt like children. We also visited the pavilions of different countries in Epcot Center. At that time, I swore to show Disney World to my children and bring my family to see the United States of America. And it was Mr. Pete Cofer, one of the outstanding persons whom I was able to meet on the path of my life who has inspired me to do this.

Two years later, Pete showed up for a Kazkat board meeting in the city of Zhezkazgan, Kazakhstan, where his new friends did their utmost to return his kindness. When the meeting was done, it was time to eat; his hosts set up a yurt, the traditional dwelling favored by the ancient nomads of the region, by the side of a lake. Among the exotic delicacies served was shashlik, hunks of marinated meat, typically lamb, impaled on skewers and cooked over hot coals. This meat, however, was no ordinary shashlik; it was saiga, a prehistoric antelope that survives only on the Russian steppes, parts of Kazakhstan, and in western Mongolia. From that day on, Pete, only half joking, would insist on saiga shashlik whenever he visited Kazakhstan. He took a fancy to Kazakh watermelons, a particularly juicy and sweet variety of the fruit. He did a calculation, Bulat Abdrakhmanov recalled, using his slide rule to determine how much it would cost him to ship a load of melons to Georgia, where watermelons are as common as ticks.

Across the former Soviet Union, there are Pete Cofer stories, still remembered and retold with delight. "One time, Pete arrived in Moscow on a Sunday dressed in blue jeans and a shirt suitable for travel," Tanya recalled. (Keep in mind Cofer rarely traveled in casual dress, so afraid was he of losing his luggage.) "But for the second time in a week his luggage was lost. He had a very important meeting with a customer on Monday morning. But all he had was his briefcase with his slide rule and papers. Let me explain that this was the time when all the stores in Moscow were empty. Everything was in short supply. Even if you could find something in the store by good luck, then you should stay in a long line and catch whatever was available and maybe not in your size at all. There was nothing in big sizes.

"Pete's only option was to discuss this with Dr. Belij. Dr. Belij said he had some brand new clothing and would bring them to the hotel on Monday morning. As I said, the meeting was extremely important and could not be postponed. On Monday, Belij showed up at the hotel. Pete smiled, put on the clothes and smiled again.

"'I'm skinnier than you are and my waist is thinner!' he said to Dr. Belij. Even though all the clothes fit, the belt was a little loose. We took a picture—these two big men standing side-by-side and Pete showing that his waist is smaller in size. As it turned out, the meeting was very productive."

In June 1992, Pete arrived in Artyomovsk in the Ukraine. Artyomovsk Non-Ferrous Metal Works wished to purchase a rod mill. The finalists were Southwire and one other competitor. At one point, Pete was in the middle of a particularly grueling discussion with a group of Artyomovsk engineers (Tanya was translating) when Gennady Aguzhen, the company's general director, a very busy and very formal man, showed up and announced, "We are having lunch together. Not at the plant."

To Pete's delight, he was driven to a clearing in the forest where a small table covered by a white tablecloth had been laid out. Gennady Aguzhen appeared in casual clothes and presented Pete with a bouquet of forest flowers. "Today, we are celebrating your birthday!" He also handed Pete a birthday present, a clock, adding, "We are happy that a person like you has been born to the world." In a photograph taken at the time, Aguzhen is staring intently at Cofer to see if he understands the "clock-birthday" pun.

"Of course, Pete understood," Tanya remembered. "And I feel that establishing such good and friendly relations was a step towards signing a contract. Pete's competitor was coming to Artyomovsk the next week, but the customer finally selected Southwire's SCR system." So impressed was Aguzhen that he intercepted Pete's car en route to the airport, feted him with another picnic meal and a bottle of the local champagne.

In Eastern Europe, Pete may have found the safe haven he could no longer find at home. Everyone smoked! Smoking was important, even necessary. Like vodka, part of the culture. "It is a common habit, said Tanya in a 2011 letter. "Many Russians have been and still are heavy smokers." This "culture of nagging someone to quit," she went on to explain, that had taken root in the United States, simply does not exist in Russia. "It would have been considered very disrespectful," she said, "to even think about making a comment about smoking to Pete Cofer."

In February 1993, Pete was on the road again in the former Soviet Union. This time he traveled to Kandalaksha City, a thousand miles north of Moscow close by the Arctic Circle. He was negotiating the sale of an SCR casting machine to the Kandalaksha Aluminum Works (KAZ). Accompanying him were Dr. Belij, Dr. Anatoly V. Minkin, formerly with the Soviet Union's Design and Research Institute of Metallurgical Machine-Building, an expert in the design of Russian rolling mills, and Tanya Golubeva.

Cofer's colleagues knew from long experience that it was much easier to travel by train from Moscow to Kandalaksha. Flying north to Murmansk involved risky weather and a 150-mile drive on treacherous roads in the dead of the Russian winter. Cofer insisted on flying. He never explained why, but on a previous train trip to visit a prospective customer in Riga, Latvia, he'd spent the night walking and smoking in the train's corridors. Asked why, he grumbled, "Your trains are too short for me!" In fact, the berths are short and very uncomfortable.

In any event, there were no flights from Moscow to Murmansk. The group settled on a flight to mountainous Kirovsk (125 miles from Kandalaksha) with a layover in Petrozavodsk, a nearby city. They flew aboard an ancient, shaky, and deafeningly loud prop plane, most likely a World War II-era Ilyushin12 or Antonov AN24. The heater didn't work, and it was -30° Fahrenheit on the ground. Freezing, they took turns nipping from a tiny flask of cognac Belij had in his bag; for food they shared a chocolate bar Tanya had in her purse.

A driver—none too intelligent-looking, one of the passengers recalled—in a yellow minivan met them in Kirovsk, and off they went. It was the middle of nowhere; it was snowing heavily, and the roads were icy and all but empty of traffic. As if on cue, the van lurched to one side and thumped to a halt.

"Flat tire," the driver shrugged.

They were still ninety miles from Kandalaksha. They sat there—the van had no heater—and began to freeze. Dr. Anatoly Minkin picked up the story: "I was still thinking, 'What has happened? How has it happened? And why it has happened to us?' At this moment, I saw Pete Cofer already outside of the bus, on the road, helping the driver to roll a wheel! It was really very cold; there was a strong, icy wind blowing, and Pete had a beautiful coat, but not appropriate, not warm enough for this temperature.

"He had a very light cap and no gloves. And he was helping to lift the bus with a jack to install the spare tire! And it turned out that the spare wheel does not match! It was from some other bus and the (lug) nuts had to be different. May I say it again—minus 30 degrees, second half of the day, it'll be getting dark soon because the days above the Arctic Circle are very short, and the nights are long. No cars on the road. Finally, a truck shows up and stops. Its driver looked at us, asked a few questions and said, 'If I meet someone, I'll ask to send the assistance.' Of course, no one came to help.

"Pete Cofer and the driver continued to work on the wheel. Dr. Belij tried to assist, but Cofer said, 'Two men are enough for the job.' Then Dr. Belij gave his scarf to Pete to keep him a little warmer. And they did it! We can only guess how, but the van was able to move, slowly, around fifty kilometers per hour. But it moved. We came to Kandalaksha around 9:00 p.m. It was dark, and the driver brought us to a boardinghouse, a nice building with very nice and clean rooms where the KAZ people used to stay on vacations. There were no people around, only a person on duty to show us the rooms. Dr. Belij checked all the rooms available and selected the warmest room for Pete."

The next morning, Pete was up bright and early and ready for his first meeting. As Anatoly Minkin watched in amazement, "Pete received questions from knowledgeable people who have been running their mill for years and who were willing to have an updated mill and to learn more about its strong points. When Pete gave answers, he opened his notebook, took the pencil and started to draw figures, small drawings and sketches. It was like magic! He gave extensive answers; he liked to discuss details. He could answer the most complicated question practically on the spot. He has used his logarithmic scale (slide rule) to make calculations and to convert non-metric units of measurements into metric system units."

The next day on a short tourist trip to the frigid White Sea, Pete whipped off his hat and announced to the amazed Russians, "I am warm because I have a warm heart!" Needless to say, he closed that deal.

Pete, Bellij, Tanya, Milton Berry, Ken Kinard, Bill Brunson, Ken Askin and other SCR team members would all remain good friends. The Russians, Ukrainians, Kazakhs, and others all made regular pilgrimages to Carrollton for training and consultations . . . and, of course, to see Pete Cofer. On occasion, they ate and socialized with the Cofer family.

One time, members of the Kazkat delegation brought Dott Cofer a gift much prized in their homeland: a wolf pelt. The Kazkat engineer, Bulat Abdrakhmanov, a man with the rare ability to speak directly from his heart, remembered a family dinner Pete arranged at the Sunset Hills Country Club. "Everything was solemn and beautiful. There I saw the fields for playing golf for the first time. Pete made a joke saying then that we could feel as millionaires because this was the club for millionaires!"

At one point, Abdrakhmanov was startled to see Kay's daughter, Lindsey, sitting in a high chair sipping a cup of ice water. "I was concerned that she may have sore throat, and said about this. I was comforted—her mom said that little children in America get accustomed to ice from a small age."

On another trip overseas, Pete and Larry White were in Belgium working on a joint venture when they met up with Dr. Bellij and Tanya and treated themselves to a few days R&R. "We all rented a van and went to the Tour de France," White recalled with a smile. "I remember we watched *The Bodyguard* on the VCR. Pete had a genuine affection for all these people and for Tanya as a human being. Maybe a sadness because of the circumstances she was in. At the time, it was so hard to earn a living in Russia." Pete's concern and affection took root among his daughters, particularly Kay Cofer Horton, who would continue to correspond and exchange memories, family photos, and emails with Tanya for the next twenty years.

CHAPTER 21

Daddy wasn't very expressive. I wish he'd shared more about his life. He could be funny or he could be serious, but to just express his true feelings and emotions was hard for him.

—ANN COFER VOLLE

AS THE YEARS WORE ON, PETE RETURNED to Carrollton after each trip just a little more tired, a little short of breath, jet-lagged, maybe nursing a cold or some other viral infection that swept through airliners of the day. (The time would come when epidemiologists at the Centers for Disease Control in Atlanta would recognize that jetliners, more than mosquitoes or other exotic infectious agents, were the principal "vector" transporting serious illnesses—influenza, malaria, encephalitis, diphtheria, polio, tuberculosis—into developed countries where they had long been considered vanished.)

Things were changing. When he was a younger man, Pete would barge through the door of the Highland Avenue house lugging his black briefcase and shiny, copper-sheathed suitcase. (Hazel Sprewell ordered the suitcases special for him at Mori's Luggage in Atlanta.) All four of his daughters would be lined up at the front door, faces scrubbed, teeth sparkling, and hair brushed until it hurt. The two youngest girls, Ann and Kay, didn't much like Dott's hair-brushing drill, but they'd stand there, bursting with excitement to see what gifts and treats Daddy had brought them from faraway places.

Pete never failed them. In his suitcase were sets of *matryoshka*, wooden Russian peasant dolls that fit inside each other, or maybe bright Japanese kimonos, Belgian chocolates, a hula skirt, or the neat little traveler's kits the airlines supplied to their business-class travelers. "We always had great show-and-tell outfits at school," remembered youngest daughter, Ann Volle. "Really, the neatest stuff."

He could not resist a joke even in his rare tender moments. He surprised Dott one year with a beautiful diamond ring but hid it in the grassy pate of a Chia Pet. When Teflon pots came on the market, he wanted Dott to have a complete set. Then, realizing she might not be overly thrilled with such a Christmas gift, he had Amy secretly scatter one hundred individual dollar bills inside the pots.

On the road, Pete didn't neglect his mother or his adult sisters, Teddy and Nancy, plying them with gifts of chocolate and pear honey from Russia, Japanese knickknacks, and every variety of Indian and Korean tchotchke. And on one occasion, he sent them ceramic elephants from China. "Pete said they were the ugliest, funniest things he ever saw," remembered Nancy Cates.

On Highland Avenue, what should have been leisurely Saturday mornings for the girls—TV and pajamas and cereal—were transformed into boot camps when Pete was home. No one was allowed to sleep in. Each daughter had a round of chores to accomplish: pulling weeds, cleaning gutters, mowing grass. After inspecting their work, he'd often drive them to his office, where he'd pick up his mail or a report Hazel had prepared while he was traveling. Then maybe a tour of the clanging, overheated rod mill where they'd all don outsized protective hard hats and safety glasses. Then it was off to Red's Barbershop to get their shoes shined and maybe, if they were lucky, a 10¢ Coca-Cola from Red's soda machine. Pete referred to the world's most famous soft drink as a "bottle of dope." Candy, to Cofer, was "pogey-bait." The girls never understood why, but it was a slang term from his Marine Corps days.

"Daddy had a name for everything and everyone," remembered Ann. She was "Scooter." Sister Kay was "Abraham" (except when she questioned his authority, then she was "Rebellion"). Amy was "Olive Oyl." Jean was "Wilhelmina." None of these names were obvious or meaningful except to Cofer. Inexplicably, he called the little girl next door "Sam Jones" and pestered the bewildered six-year-old with the question "When are you getting married?"

Some Saturdays, when the household chores were well in hand, and whatever hobby or task he was working on was in abeyance, Pete would walk out into the front yard and, in Ann's memory, "make a big whistle." As if under a spell, all the kids in the neighborhood would come running. He'd pile them into his station wagon and head to the Stop and Shop on Shady Grove Road, or the A&W stand he labeled the "root beer place," and treat everyone to ice cream.

Cofer preferred to return from his travels on Saturdays to give himself a day to rest up. On Sunday nights, when he was younger, he and the girls would fix "breakfast for dinner," whipping up eggs, French toast, or waffles while Dott took the night off. Afterward, he'd lie on the living room floor and his daughters, at the time little girls, would run circles around his lanky frame. "Suddenly he'd reach up!" Ann remembered, "and grab one of us and tickle her while the rest of us screamed and laughed and all of that!" Another of his daughters added, "That was Daddy. Either joking or disciplining."

Many years later, when his health was failing, Pete, then affectionately known as "Grumps," would play that same game with Kay Cofer Horton's kids. "They were little-bitty," she remembered. "Daddy would lay on the floor like Gulliver and they'd crawl all over him."

Kay remembered carrying her father's tools while he worked on his handyman projects. "There was a little creek in the front yard. We'd jump back and forth across it, and the sides of the creek would always cave in and stop up the water. So Daddy made a little stone bridge across the creek and tried to shore up the walls. Then he added a little stone bench. Then a bigger stone bench in the backyard. He chiseled and cut the stone himself.

He wouldn't let me hit anything or break anything with the hammer."

When she was very young, Ann loved to watch her father shave. "He'd put me on the counter and put shaving cream on my face and give me a razor with no blade," she recalled. "I'd shave just like him."

Ann and Kay, who were years younger than Jean and Amy, and say they felt Pete's absence more acutely than the "big" girls. Today, both are mothers themselves, but they remain steadfastly Daddy's girls. "My sisters were already into other things," Ann insisted. "Whenever Daddy was home, I wanted to be with him. I had a camaraderie with him that I didn't have with my older sisters or my mom. Of course, I loved Mom. She was always there for me. I don't know if it was because my father traveled so much and I missed him so much, or whether I did have a special connection."

Amy and Jean took good advantage of Ann's favored status. "If they wanted money, it was, 'Ann, go get twenty dollars.' And I'd go sit in his lap. 'Daddy, can I have some money?' I'd whisper. It didn't work very often, but sometimes it did." When she was in college, and her father's health was deteriorating, Ann would drive home on the weekends, content to sit on the couch while Pete stared at the television. "We just kind of hung out together," she recalled. "We didn't really have to have a conversation."

Often, there was a real need to talk, understand, or connect with the man who was their husband or father, but no matter how hard Dott and the girls tried, there were places in Pete Cofer they could not reach. "He just wasn't very expressive," another of his daughters remembered. "I wish he'd shared more about his life, but he never did. Daddy could be funny or he could be serious, but to just express true feelings and emotions was hard for him."

All these years later, it falls to others to fill in some of those empty spaces. "With his girls, oh my goodness!" Hazel Sprewell gushes. "Pete just loved them to death!" Hazel, as suggested, became far more than Cofer's secretary. She was his confidante and guardian angel for twenty-four years and probably knew him as well as anyone. "He wanted them to go to any school they wanted. I know Pete talked to Mr. Richards about that one time— I saw it in his notes—and he told Mr. Richards that he thought it was more important for girls to be well educated than for boys."

Obviously, there was much more to the inner Pete than he allowed to surface. And of the negative, much less. For example, he appears to have enjoyed playing the role of curmudgeon and cheapskate. Of the many stories that grew up around Cofer's frugality, one has to do with his daughters' college tuition.

"He'd require every one of them to submit a budget," remembered Hazel Sprewell. "I mean it had to be 'to the wire!'" That is certainly true, as is the fact that Pete pinched pennies long before his daughters were of college age. With all legends and parables, the deeper truth is often disguised in the telling. "When we turned ten, Daddy took each of us to the bank and opened a checking account," remembered Ann. "We got a VIP card with our picture so we could write checks. As soon as we were old enough, Daddy had us working summers. We couldn't really work until we were sixteen, so he had us do yard work. Lots of yard work, and often for punishment. When we were older, he made a point of sitting down with us to do our income taxes. He'd hammer us: 'You need to save! You need to save at least 10 percent of your income.' I always dreaded the income tax preparation. Here I am sixteen years old, and Daddy's demanding, 'What's in your savings account?' You don't like having to do that kind of stuff at that age."

Sister Kay remembers a similar drill. "When I went to college, my parents provided my tuition and living expenses. The word from Dad was, 'No budget, no money.' Each month, I had to submit a budget for the following month, a comparison of my budget versus actual spending for the previous month. I went to West Georgia College for two years and then transferred to Georgia State University. At this point, I had to rent an apartment in Atlanta because there were no dorms. Suddenly, there were a lot of categories—rent, phone, utilities, and so on. I'm a numbers person, so it wasn't that difficult, but I still remember the month my gas bill was very high—it was in the winter!—and I'd gone way over budget. I was shaking in my boots to have to show Daddy the figures.

"To my surprise, he wasn't upset. It was the principle of doing a budget and knowing what was going on that was important. He taught me a lot about financial responsibility. I now realize a lot of what Daddy did was trying to train us for the future."

When they graduated, Pete bought each daughter a car. As one remembered, "a slightly used, almost new car." At this point, Pete announced they were "officially off his payroll." (Not quite true. Cofer carefully managed a trust fund for each of the girls—mostly money inherited from the Ingrams, Dott's parents. One daughter insisted her dad did not get around to mentioning this trust until she was thirty years old. Pete no doubt figured the dizzying idea of a pile of unearned cash would tempt the girls from the path of frugality.)

The "buying of the car" ritual was another life lesson. Ann and her sisters got to meet the master negotiator Southwire relied on to go head-to-head with the world's most stubborn and cantankerous men. "He started off saying, 'This is how much I'll spend,'" remembered Ann. "Then he and I went shopping at a Volkswagen dealer my sister knew in Atlanta. The car Daddy picked was a no-frills VW Golf.

"I don't want that car!"

"What!"

"I don't want it."

Ann instead chose a white 1985 Jetta sedan. She convinced herself she'd be doing a lot of traveling for her new job. The Jetta was roomier. It had more trunk space. But it cost $9,000, which was $1,000 more than what Pete had budgeted.

"Nope."

"Daddy, I have a job. I'll take out a loan."

At the word "loan," Cofer went ballistic. "He said it was dumb to borrow money right out of college," she recalled. "Besides, he believed you only pay cash for cars."

The two went round and round, matching each other in stubbornness.

Pete and Dott stand alongside their daughters at the Cofer Center opening in April 1992. Daughters, back row left to right: Ann, Kay, and Jean. Jean's daughter Brooke is standing front left and Kay is holding her daughter Lindsay. Pete believed in teaching the value of money at an early age. When their daughters were ten years old, he took each to the bank and helped them open a checking account. He taught them all about budgets and saving, holding them each accountable for their spending while they were at college.

"I didn't back down," Ann remembered. "So we kept looking. And I still didn't back down."

Pete realized he was getting nowhere. He folded his cards. Almost.

"Okay, get the Jetta."

"Dad, really?"

"With a proviso. I'll loan you the extra $1,000."

"Okay, it's a deal."

Good as his word, after Pete signed off on the Jetta, he handed Ann a stack of deposit slips for his bank account.

"Daddy was a tough negotiator," Ann recalled many years later. "He wanted to make the decision for me, but I didn't let him."

Ann owned the reliable little four-cylinder for ten years and put 150,000 miles on it.

"See, I was right!" she later said. "You had to stand up to Daddy a little, and he'd concede a point—if it was reasonable."

She paused and then added, "I got what I wanted, but he did make me pay for it."

It was the same approach Pete took with his Southwire clients.

When Dott traveled with Pete on one of his business trips overseas, she saw firsthand how demanding his schedule was: one meeting after another with only evenings available for dinner or a show.

Chapter 22

Think of Pete's life as a rambling house with different wings and rooms.

PETE COFER SPENT THIRTY-ODD YEARS CRISSCROSSING the globe for Southwire. In all that time, Dott Cofer insists she only traveled abroad with her husband one time. Almost a half century later, she still remembers the conversation in which Pete extended the invitation. It began when he arrived home one evening and pulled a book about Europe from his briefcase.

"Maybe you might want to look through this."

"Right. Maybe I'll get to go sometime."

"How about August 16th?"

"What?"

"Dott, I've already booked it."

"Oh, Pete!"

When the big day came, Pete's mother, Mariah, and his Aunt Floy (Mariah's sister-in-law) arrived from middle Georgia to babysit the girls. "It was the only time I'd ever been out of the country," Dott recalled. "There was a meeting in Amsterdam. A lot of the other engineers' wives were there too, but, unfortunately, we didn't get together until the last day. So I wandered around by myself with this little map in my hand. I didn't speak any language. And they didn't speak a lot of English back then."

In Amsterdam, Dott had an epiphany. She saw a side of her much-traveled husband she'd never seen before: not only a man totally immersed in the demands of his job, but also the demands he made on himself. "Honestly, I'd think," Dott recalled in 2011, 'Oh he's getting to go on these trips all over the world! He gets to go, and here I am, stuck at home raising the kids.' Well, I sure found out different. Pete met somebody for breakfast; he had a 10 o'clock meeting; he met somebody else for lunch. At 2 o'clock, he was in another meeting! In the evening, we'd go out to dinner or a play somebody took us to. Other than that, he was working all the time. I got a whole different perspective."

That same trip provides another insight into Cofer. When the couple arrived back in Carrollton, Dott noticed Pete seemed glum and out of sorts. "I finally asked him what was wrong," she remembered. "Turned out he felt so guilty about leaving our daughters behind, he went out and bought them a trampoline! He thought he wasn't being fair to take me and not do something for them."

Soon enough, the familiar one-track workaholic reappeared. Ann remembered asking if she could accompany her dad on an upcoming trip to the Soviet Union. She'd graduated from college and was up to date on her car payments.

"I begged him to take me," she recalled. "'Please, Daddy, please take me!'
"He wouldn't."

Pete would occasionally invite overseas guests to the house for drinks, dinner, or a cookout. Among them were Southwire's Japanese agent Teruma Hamada, Ukrainian-born head of the Soviet cable and wire ministry Diamar Belij, and Tanya. There were a number of dinners at the Sunset Hills Country Club, where Dott, all the daughters, and (in later years) a grandchild or two would be included. One time, the girls met an international celebrity when their father brought home acclaimed opera singer Kiri Jeanette Te Kanawa, a Maori from New Zealand whose husband, Desmond Park, did business with Southwire.

--- ❦ ---

Throughout their lives, Dott and her daughters heard scarcely a word about Cofer's military experiences. Such closemouthed behavior is typical of most World War II veterans. The reasons, whatever the war, are obvious. Today, when the Cofer women look back, they realize that they actually knew very little about Pete's service, his job or overseas travels, his crises, technical triumphs, and setbacks. Nuts-and-bolts engineering does not lend itself to family dinner conversation, but even with that in mind, Pete at home was hardly the nonstop conversationalist he was elsewhere. Certainly, much of this behavior has to do with the times he lived in, and the "men's work/women's work" divide that existed in Pete's brain. Family members, like most readers, will encounter many of the anecdotes and many of the people appearing in this book for the first time. Pete's life was, in fact, a rambling house with different wings and rooms open or off limits at different times to different people.

It is no surprise that Cofer's extensive travels to Communist-bloc and troubled Third World countries . . . his closemouthed approach to his extraordinary military experiences at the close of World War II . . . the appearance of Russians, Kazakhs, Chinese, and other exotica in Carrollton inevitably triggered rumors and speculation by Dott, Harold Miles, and many others, that there had to be more to Southwire's international footprint than met the eye. The peripatetic Pete Cofer, they thought, must be some kind of undercover agent, a real-life Maxwell Smart living a cloak-and-dagger double life.

This was the Cold War era when James Bond novels were popular, when Americans installed bomb shelters not hot tubs, when Nikita Khrushchev's supposed threat ("We will bury you") was taken to heart, and when the 1962 Cuban Missile Crisis almost took the world over the edge. In truth, the nuclear arms race only abated when cooler heads in Washington, Beijing, and Moscow finally realized that the nightmare scenario of MAD ("Mutually Assured Destruction") was inching closer to reality.

Like Roy Richards Sr., Pete Cofer embraced a robust patriotism and an utter commitment to his country. He was certainly in the right places at the right times and met the right people. During the Cold War, it was not unusual for agency people to debrief businessmen returning from places of interest or unrest. If so, Pete Cofer might have returned the call.

Was Cofer a CIA man?

Those in a position to know insist he was not.

CHAPTER 23

Pete just didn't want to quit smoking.

—DOTT COFER

AS THE FOUR COFER SISTERS GREW OLDER, and warnings about the dangers of tobacco filtered into the general population, they couldn't help but notice that their father's smoking continued unabated . . . that it was impossible to imagine Daddy without a burning cigarette in his hand . . . that his clothes and cars literally reeked of tobacco smoke . . . that his shirts and suit pants were peppered with ash and cigarette burns.

The Surgeon General's 1964 warning about the dangers of smoking and the linkage between tar, nicotine, and lung cancer came and went. Pete paid no mind to the warnings, even joked about them. Wasn't a "coffin nail" a familiar definition of a cigarette? Pete wasn't alone in his denial. One out of two Americans smoked, this despite the fact that half the population *believed* that smoking caused cancer. He might have recognized that it was becoming more difficult to climb the stairs to his fourth floor office, to lug his bags through all those airport terminals, to walk around the square in Carrollton or to sightsee on China's Great Wall. Perhaps he accepted these facts as—so many in denial do—simply a part of growing older.

Like tens of millions of Americans, Cofer was in the grip of a powerful chemical dependency we now know was nurtured and enhanced by the tobacco industry's careful manipulation of nicotine; a habit that could be indulged at any convenience store for less than 60¢ a pack. An addiction that researchers at the American Heart Association and elsewhere concluded was more powerful than heroin or cocaine. He shared this dependency with billions of people around the globe.

"Hell," Pete would have assured himself every time he visited Asia, Western Europe or the Soviet Union, "Who doesn't smoke? And what business does my employer or government have trying to tell me what to do or not do when it comes to my personal life?"

This is a very common but flawed argument, one that motorcyclists who refuse to wear helmets often make, forgetting that when they atomize their brains in spectacular spills, it falls to the government and taxpayers to underwrite their long-term care. Despite his ingrained respect for authority, this side of Cofer was purely libertarian and bridled against all antismoking restraints.

His girls, who were bright and curious and very concerned about Daddy's health, would certainly have read the warning printed on the back of each pack of Cofer's Marlboros:

Pete was consistent, driven, and unrelenting in every aspect of his life and career.

"Cigarettes may be hazardous to your health." Before long, they'd be banging heads with him over his cigarettes.

Pete didn't stop. Maybe he couldn't stop, the same way he couldn't slow down or relax. His job was stressful, the traveling was exhausting, the give-and-take of never-ending negotiations frustrating; the responsibility he felt to his Southwire team and the Richards family all-consuming. He was a proud man, even a courageous man, and no doubt wanted to be the go-to guy, "the man in the arena," as President Theodore Roosevelt eloquently phrased it:

> The credit belongs to the man who is actually in the arena, whose face is marred by dust and sweat and blood; who strives valiantly; who errs, who comes short again and again, because there is no effort without error and shortcoming; but who does actually strive to do the deeds . . .

Roy Richards detested smoking. "It literally drove my father mad," remembered Jim Richards. "And Pete was one of these guys that you could smell smoke on him when he came through the front door. My father put up with that. He wouldn't put up with it for many people, but he knew Pete was unique."

Light a cigarette—the act was second nature to Cofer—and instantly he'd experience relaxation and calm even as his mind became sharper and more alert, his brain and nervous system awash in a warm bath of neurotransmitters and hormones—acetylcholine, norepinephrine, epinephrine, vasopressin, arginine, beta-endorphin. On the other hand, nicotine was continually elevating his blood pressure, constricting his arteries, making it harder for his heart to pump, triggering the release of fat and cholesterol into his bloodstream. Cofer's diet was already unhealthy, and he began to put on weight.

"Pete's most obvious characteristic was his intellect and business acumen," recalled Ken Kinard, who has struggled with heart disease for much of his adult life. "But if he had a fault, if you looked for one, it had to be tobacco. This man would light one cigarette with another!

"I remember it clearly. He'd have old Hal Jones in the conference room with him, and his first secretary, Mabel Gable, all three puffing away. It used to kill me to go in there with these guys. Pete's cigarette would get short. Hal's got a full one. Pete would pick up a new one and light off Hal's. It would never go out. I don't know if he was a two-pack or three-pack or a four-pack-a day guy. But I can tell you it was sequential."

Ironically, it was Dott's health that had some impact on her husband's habit. She was diagnosed with breast cancer in 1967. At the time, Pete, very worried, asked her oncologist, "What can I do to help?"

"Never smoke around her."

"Really?"

"From then on," Dott later recalled, "Pete smoked outside."

It wasn't much, but it was something. He had a chair on the patio, and for the rest of his life he'd go out there to light up. As it turned out, Dott's disease went into remission after treatment.

In 1988, the major airlines, aware of the threat and potential liability posed by secondary smoke, began banning smoking on domestic flights. Over the next few years, the ban spread to Delta Airlines and other carriers' international flights, literally imprisoning Pete Cofer hour after endless hour in an aluminum tube 35,000 feet above the earth.

Hugh Wallace

PART III

CRISIS AND REBIRTH

Roy Richards presents the Distinguished Service Award to his Chief Engineer, Pete Cofer.

CHAPTER 24

In any war, there are always unintended consequences.

By 1979, THE FINAL YEAR OF JIMMY CARTER'S presidency, Pete Cofer and his band of SCR men had sold 22 copper rod mills. They were in the process of closing deals on another half-dozen in Korea, West Germany, Japan, and China. Business was so robust that the SCR division was racking up an estimated 10 percent of Southwire's annual profit. Cofer saw blue skies and clear sailing in the overseas markets, but storm clouds were gathering at home.

The 1960s had been a tumultuous decade, a stark contrast to the peace and tranquility of the 1950s, during which Pete Cofer had come to maturity. The 1960s witnessed the coming of age of the civil rights movement and the assassinations of John F. Kennedy, Robert Kennedy, and Dr. Martin Luther King. Woodstock, Weathermen, the moon landing, the sexual revolution, the escalation of the Vietnam War, and the furious protest movement it engendered.

In the 1970s, the baby boomers, that most indulged and self-involved generation, were coming into their own. By the decade's end, it seemed as if some long-overdue bill was finally coming due. A string of spectacular setbacks—the humiliating and costly defeat in Southeast Asia, the Watergate scandal, the 1973 Arab Oil Embargo, the 1973–1974 recession, 1979 Iranian Revolution, and, in its wake, a second energy crisis and the hostage-taking at the American embassy in Tehran—engendered the "malaise" President Carter famously sensed among the American public. Divorce rates began to spiral; crime and drug abuse spread; AIDS was moving inexorably out of the villages and truck stops of central Africa. Over the next twenty years, the epidemic would kill 25 million people worldwide before it slowed. As the Rolling Stones said it, chaos was "just a shot away."

It is reasonable to assume that Roy Richards and Pete Cofer, like others of their generation, were aware of and troubled by these seismic changes and the lack of leadership seemingly at every level of governance. Their response, the only response their generation ever knew, was to dig in, work harder, and fight to hold a steady course.

A good part of the malaise was economic. In 1973, inflation ratcheted up to 5 percent from an average 2.6 percent in the 1960s. By 1979, it was at 11 percent and rising. In October 1979, hoping to avoid a full-blown meltdown, Federal Reserve Chairman Paul Volcker implemented a round of dramatic interest rate hikes, the classic Keynesian antidote for runaway inflation.

The impact of the interest rate escalations instantly struck home in Carrollton. Roy Richards had been riding a decades-long wave of growth and prosperity when, in 1980, interest rates surged past 18 percent. Two years later, the prime rate—the interest rate commercial banks charge their most credit-worthy customers—stood at 21.5 percent, unprecedented in peacetime history. Like a medieval healer, Volcker was slowly bleeding inflation out of the fevered economy. It later fell to 6 percent and continued to drop into the late 1980s. Interest rates declined, and Volcker's triumph over inflation is credited with helping usher in the broad-based economic boom of the next decades.

In any war, there are always unintended consequences.

CHAPTER 25

It was momentum . . . growth . . . expansion.

—JIM RICHARDS

A PRIVATELY HELD COMPANY, SOUTHWIRE HAD no ability to sell bonds or issue publicly traded stock. Growth was fueled by access to credit: bank loans. Over the years, Roy Richards had nurtured long-term relationships with more than two dozen banks. In 1980, as interest rates soared, Southwire had drawn between "$20 to $60 million" on its lines of credit, money Richards used to fund growth and expansion, run the day-to-day operations, and seed outside investments.

"As my father's success continued in the late 1970s, he wanted to integrate in every conceivable direction," explained Jim Richards. To that end, in addition to wire-making, Southwire had created Cofer's SCR unit; it had partnered in an enormously profitable aluminum smelter in Hawesville, Kentucky; there was a major, though increasingly troublesome aluminum wire and cable mill investment—Sural—in Venezuela. In Carrollton, a car dealership, a sawmill, a trucking division, a jet.

In keeping with Roy Sr.'s embrace of technology as the key to trumping the competition, machinery and equipment in the plants was continuously upgraded, expanded, speeded up. Cofer's continuing improvement of the SCR mills is just one example of this overall "bigger, stronger, faster" strategy.

Southwire's successes riding a thirty-year head of steam and dependent on the free flow of credit. "It was momentum . . . growth . . . expansion," remembered Jim Richards. Indeed, side-by-side comparisons of aerial photographs of the Carrollton plant in the go-go years resemble microscopic slides depicting runaway cell division. "Throughout his entire life, Roy Richards Sr. was a builder," remembered Ken Kinard. "He built and built. There was no time for consolidation. At one point, our growth was so great, our profits weren't sufficient to pay interest upon our new investments. That's what got us into trouble."

Every loan that had ever been made to Southwire had been paid off in a timely fashion. Business was good. The company was growing. Why look back? Collateral for Southwire's borrowing was its inventory of aluminum. In Kentucky, the Hawesville smelter poured out the metal like a printing press. Aluminum is a commodity, and like all commodities, subject to the gyrations of the marketplace.

The price of aluminum collapsed.

Given the economic slowdown and soaring interest rates, it was inevitable that Southwire's lenders would come calling. When trouble came, it came quickly and with devastating impact. "Manufacturers Hanover looked at all their loans," remembered Roy Richards Jr. "When they got to Southwire, which, frankly, all our banks had ignored, they saw that we had a big chunk of aluminum (by some estimates as much as 100 million pounds) valued on our balance sheet at 75¢ a pound. The market price was 55¢."

Southwire would have to write off that difference, a $20 to $40 million charge. "When that calculation was applied to our balance sheet," said Roy Jr., "Southwire's entire financial condition was instantly at risk." Other lenders piled on. Lloyds Bank, Chase Manhattan, Deutsche Bank, Citibank, Manufacturers Hanover Trust Company, a host of smaller institutions all calling in their loans. For the first time in his life, Roy Richards Sr. seemed at a loss. Among other missteps, he'd blended his individual and business holdings indiscriminately. Now the creditors were coming after him personally. "At one point, we received a demand letter from Manny Hanny," Roy Jr. remembered.

"It said, 'You've got seven days to pay us.'"

CHAPTER 26

*There were primary problems and peripheral problems
and tertiary problems. The most important consequence
was that Dad would have to declare bankruptcy.*

—ROY RICHARDS JR.

PETE COFER HAD A SIMPLE BUT EFFECTIVE APPROACH to problem-solving. In the course of his long career, he'd used it to cut through obstacles, energize flagging employees, overwhelm competitors, penetrate the fog of bureaucracy and institutional miasma with laser-like clarity. He called it "Eliminating Excuses."

"In Pete's straightforward way of looking at things," remembered Roy Richards Jr., "if you had a problem or something that couldn't get done, the only way to fix it was to eliminate all excuses."

If anything, the crisis threatening Southwire served to energize Cofer. He was a man who had much more than his career or a financial stake invested in Southwire's success. Southwire was his "baby," insist those who knew him. Additionally, Cofer's relationship with the embattled Roy Richards went far beyond employer-employee, or the oft-mentioned "right-hand man." Pete had been an extension of Richards's will, the force who converted Roy's overarching visions and grand schemes into actual industrial output. If Roy faltered, Cofer would do anything in his power to take up the slack.

"Pete was probably the most irreplaceable guy we had," remembered Jim Richards. "He had more one-on-one time with my father than anybody except Roger Schoerner." (Schoerner, a senior vice president, was one of Richards's earliest hires, arriving from Anaconda Wire and Cable. At the time, Schoerner was the only person at Southwire with a working knowledge of the wire-making business.) Cofer had a granular understanding of every aspect of the company's workings. Where others saw the approach of a cataclysmic wave, Pete, with an engineer's ability to break a problem down into parts (ponder, rework, refine, and reassemble) saw a series of components, some in synch, some wildly cacophonous. Eliminate the dissonance, and things would run smoothly again.

Cofer also viewed Roy Richards's eldest sons, Roy Jr. and Jim, who'd hung around the factory since they were teenagers, almost as wards that he was responsible for grooming. This complex mix of loyalty, experience, practicality, and genius that was Pete Cofer would play a major part in Southwire's subsequent rally.

As the banks circled, Roy Jr., a "born-again engineering student," was looking forward to his senior year at Georgia Tech. Brother Jim, a finance major, was a year behind him. Like many a young man before him, Roy Jr. had frittered away his freshman and sophomore years and was determined to put his childish ways behind him. "By then, I was finally mature and making great grades," he recalled wistfully.

The phone call, when it came, caught him by surprise. It was his father, the familiar confidence and optimism leeched out of his voice.

"Roy, would you not enroll next quarter?"

"Daddy, what's going on?"

"I need you here."

"What's going on?"

"I want you to here to help us."

Roy Jr. dropped out of school and drove home to Carrollton where his father appointed him, "technical assistant to the president," an amorphous operations slot that would grow and grow and consume him for the next twenty years. Jim Richards, whose passions were finance and strategic planning, soon followed and launched himself into the fray.

In Carrollton, things had reached full crisis mode. Each day, after the employees left, the company's top brass held emergency meetings. Years later, they would remember these meetings as the "first time Southwire officers sat down and talked to each other in a serious way about problems." Posters and bubble charts appeared on office walls, expanding—participants remembered—like those cartoon graphs where production or profit literally plummet off the chart.

Pete Cofer sat in on those meetings, smoking, scribbling notes in his black book. The organizational "silos," which Roy Sr. had intentionally kept separate, began sharing information. None of it good. "There were primary problems and peripheral problems and tertiary problems," Roy Jr. remembered. Southwire was actually the healthiest of Richards's myriad holdings. "The problem was not Southwire," Roy Jr. added. "It was far bigger. The total debt picture was three times what we thought it was and impacted all of Richards's holdings. The most important consequence was that Dad would have to declare bankruptcy. It was talked about every day, usually without him in the room."

A day came when Pete Cofer had heard enough. "Of all the people who advise your dad," he told Roy Jr., "there's one I know who can help him. His name is Allison Wade. He's the smartest attorney I know. At this point, your dad doesn't need any more meetings.

He needs protection. And defense."

The SOS went out to Allison Wade in Atlanta.

Despite its broken balance sheet, it became clear that Southwire was the likeliest of Richards's myriad enterprises (labeled by his sons "dogs and cats") to be resuscitated. There were efficiencies to be had, new markets to explore, opportunities to pursue once the economic clouds and crushing debt service lifted.

Jim and Roy Jr. gathered the collective wisdom of the lawyers and accountants, vice

Roy Richards recruited his son Roy Jr. from Georgia Tech to help him with Southwire. Richards's son Jim followed soon after. Pete and Roy Jr. (above) became very close as they worked together to strategize ways to pull Southwire out of ever-increasing debt.

presidents, and wise men, and delivered it to their father. He was unresponsive. "Dad wanted to do about 5 percent of what was recommended," Roy Jr. remembered. "It's the owner's prerogative not to solve or fix any problems. An owner can pick and choose. Dad did that. I guess some of the problems were so big and hairy, and so damn hard to solve, he dealt only with the things he could deal with. He was overwhelmed."

Roy Richards's denial was not the reluctance to face hard facts and unpleasant truths that all of us struggle with in hard times. Roy Sr. was too much of a realist for that. This ran deeper. He was a man facing the loss of everything he'd built and struggled and cared about, literally the foundation of his existence and the wellspring of his confidence. His denial suggests the soul-deep grief psychiatrist Elizabeth Kubler-Ross describes in her landmark study, *On Death and Dying*.

"It can't be happening to me."

It was happening. And there were worse things ahead. Fate is often more cruel, painful, and unfair than anyone might possibly imagine. Unknown to him, Roy Richards's own body was in rebellion. *Osteosarcoma*, a virulent and painful cancer, was fulminating in his bones.

CHAPTER 27

We'd reached the point where we weren't going to turn it around.

—ROY RICHARDS JR.

⸻

IN THE FALL OF 1982, THE UNTHINKABLE HAD BECOME inevitable. Bankruptcy seemed Roy Richards' only remaining option. Attorneys Allison Wade and Dennis Meir of the white-shoe Atlanta law firm Kilpatrick & Cody (today Kilpatrick Townsend), personally prepared the filings for Southwire, a number of subsidiary companies, and Roy Richards. Jim Richards recalled an "eighteen-inch tall stack of papers." Outstanding obligations topped an estimated $180 million at a time when such a sum was considered a staggering debt . . . when the prime rate still hovered around 15 percent. "We'd reached the point where we weren't going to turn it around," remembered Roy Jr.

The elder Richards had one card left to play. On a Friday morning, he'd dispatched one of his attorneys to bankruptcy court in Atlanta with the filings and instructions to await his personal phone call to file them in the court. He'd called a 3:00 p.m. meeting of his creditors—more than two-dozen banks—that afternoon, and reserved the Capital City Club's Peachtree Room. When the bankers arrived in Atlanta (by some accounts, nearly fifty somber men and women in pinstripes and dark suits), copies of the filings were stacked for all to see on a table next to the podium. One former Southwire executive later compared those papers to "a hand grenade with the pin pulled."

Roy Richards walked up to the podium, waited a moment for silence, and began his play. What follows is based on the recollections of Jim and Roy Richards Jr., who were both at the meeting:

> The room was full. The mood was cantankerous, to say the least, predators and prey regarding one another. Then Dad pointed to the stack of papers and said, "Gentlemen, this is a bankruptcy petition for me and everything I own. These are copies. The originals are at the courthouse with my secretary. She's waiting for my instructions to file them."
>
> When the murmuring quieted down, he continued. "If we can work this out in the next two hours, if you'll grant me some kind of moratorium, a delay or grace period on my indebtedness, then I won't have to file for bankruptcy protection." He knew the bankers were scared of a bankruptcy. They'd have to dump all this undervalued aluminum, all these factories, shut down all this stuff. There'd be a giant fight over who owed what to whom . . . who was first . . . because it was all layered in and poorly documented. Amaz-

ingly, all this money had all been loaned just on the basis of Dad's personality and handshake.

The room fell silent. After a moment, the senior guy at the biggest bank in the room said, "Mr. Richards, let us work on this a bit." There were two or three further exchanges and the bankers went into one room and we went into another. When they emerged, they said, "We can't give you everything you want, but we've agreed that we will have a standstill agreement for forty-five days until we can put in place a moratorium. Our preliminary agreement is that the moratorium might be for nine months.

The pin went back into the grenade.

Southwire tottered and then pulled back from the abyss. Roy Richards agreed to slash operating costs, sell off or shut down his failing businesses, and reduce Southwire's staggering overhead. The Venezuelan operation was first on the hit list. "We had almost nothing to show for our investment in it," Roy Jr. remembered. Manpower reductions followed. A company that prided itself on being the flagship of its community was forced, for the first time, to lay off hundreds of workers. The Atlanta newspapers got wind of the story, and Roy Richards's private humiliation became public. "It was ultra-painful," Roy Jr. remembered, "but we did it. We stuck to our religion about streamlining and cost control. And when the acute pressure finally relaxed, Daddy was able to do things in a more orderly way."

———

If you or a loved one has suffered cancer's ravages, if you've known its false hopes and lived in dread of its inexorable progress, you understand it is a disease that brooks few happy endings. Over the next two years, Southwire would begin its recovery. Roy Richards—husband, father, patriarch, and founder—would not. He was hospitalized in January 1985, debilitated by metastatic bone cancer and never set foot in his beloved office again. He passed away at Emory University Hospital on June 2, 1985. He was seventy-three years old.

Day-to-day control of Southwire passed to Roy Jr. and Jim Richards.

CHAPTER 28

There was no problem that was ever bigger than Pete Cofer.

—ROY RICHARDS JR.

———

ROY RICHARD'S DEATH WAS A CRUSHING BLOW to his family and the still-staggering company. In his early seventies and seemingly in robust health when he was taken ill, Roy Sr. would have assumed he had plenty of time to season his sons and map out a succession plan. As it turned out, he had time for none of this. Roy Jr. and Jim Richards were appointed co-presidents, with Jim Griffin, the senior vice president of sales, acting, in effect, as the third arm of a triumvirate. The boys were still grieving. They were in their early twenties, inexperienced and ill-prepared given the scope and magnitude of the problems Southwire still faced.

One of Southwire's most senior executives immediately filed a lawsuit alleging that his stock options were undervalued by millions of dollars. Another of Roy Sr.'s closest associates was enmeshed in an ethics violation that might lead to criminal charges. Lawsuits brought by the Properzi company alleging patent infringements and other violations were still simmering after seventeen years. There were labor problems, looming layoffs, safety issues, pollution concerns, bloated overhead costs, and wrangles with customers. If there was a glimmer of hope, it stood six-foot-four, was rumpled as an unmade bed, and seemed to thrive on the insoluble.

Wildly over his head and working twelve-hour days, Roy Jr. turned to Pete Cofer. "You went to see Pete," he remembered. "No matter what your title was, you went to Pete's office. He was the god of the fourth floor. I took him these problems, this huge basket of problems."

Cofer was a man of routines, regular and soothing as the tides. You could set your watch based by his arrival at Jerry's to meet his breakfast club cronies. Bring him a problem, and he'd get up from behind his desk, walk over, and sit down at his conference table with you. Not across the table, but right next to you, the big brother or the understanding dad all of us wish we had. He'd sit there, eyes blinking behind his thick glasses, smoke curling from a cigarette. Listening. Asking an occasional question.

"He had those black notebooks," Roy Jr. remembered. "He'd open up a notebook and start taking notes and fill up a page or two of careful notes and questions. Then he'd say, 'Let me work on it. I'll get back to you.' And so the meeting was over. You'd get a call from him the next day.

"'Come on back up here.'"

There were the answers, or at least a strategy to get the answers, numbers crunched, steps outlined as if the man had a supercomputer in his briefcase. Quietly and without fanfare, Cofer became Roy Jr.'s chief advisor, a role that expanded in 1987 when the board of directors appointed Roy Jr. sole president and CEO. "Then I really did lean on Pete." Roy was bright, a workaholic himself. Like his father before him, he put off marriage and family to tend to the demands of the business and was living a solitary, almost monastic life. "I just did not live then like other young single guys did," Roy later insisted. "I worked."

Who better than a tough, strapping, irreverent, ex-Marine who drank and cussed and told bawdy jokes for a role model? Like anyone who ever worked with Cofer, once in a while, Roy Jr. decided to outwork the man. "No matter how much homework I'd do," he recalled, "Pete had done three times as much. He was always better prepared than anybody else."

Cofer, by nature or volition, unwilling to express his own feelings, was extremely sensitive to the storms of self-doubt buffeting young Roy. Perhaps he wanted to share the life lessons and extraordinary experiences he'd had as a young man, but couldn't with his wife and daughters. In the course of another crisis, a betrayal that left the young CEO "wringing my hands," Pete shared the rarest of confidences: he talked about the trauma of war.

"Pete proceeded to tell me about his experiences in China at the end of World War II," Roy Jr. recalled many years later. "How he was faced with life or death decisions as a Marine in combat. He explained how he dealt with the stress of that and the burden he had to carry afterward. Telling me these stories gave me the confidence to deal with the crisis. And suddenly, my problems seemed much smaller."

The two men worked closely together for almost ten years. More than twenty-five years have passed, but retelling these stories, remembering Cofer's kindness, still has an extraordinary impact on Roy Richards Jr. "When my dad died, I had a big responsibility," he recalled, voice breaking. "I had a lot of stress on me, and Pete was . . . Pete was always there for me. I worshipped Pete. There was no problem that was ever bigger than Pete Cofer."

In the years after Roy Richards's death, Pete Cofer became not only a mentor but also a second father to Roy Richards Jr.

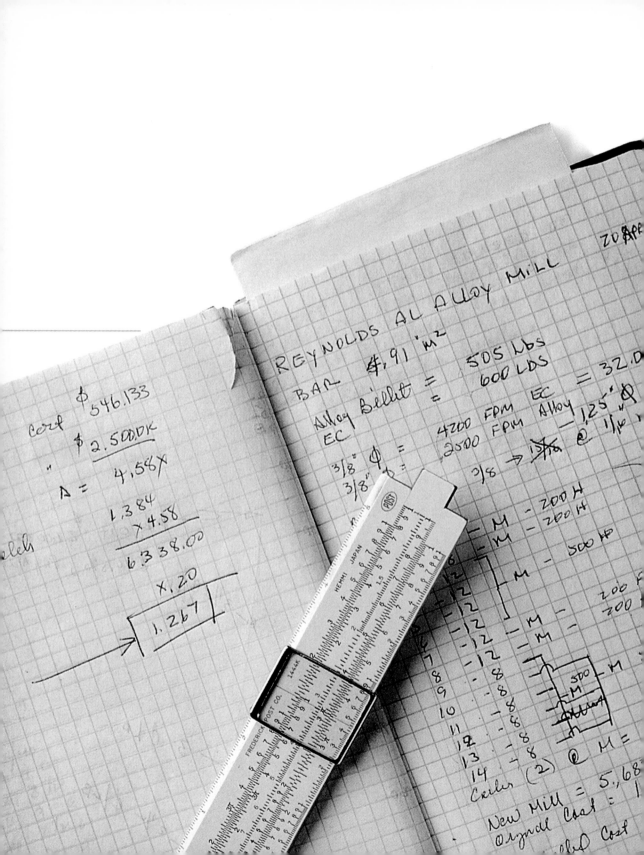

Corp $546.133

" $ 2.500.0K

A = 4.58X

1.384
X 4.58
─────
6.338.00

X.20

1.267

Right page:

REYNOLDS AL ALLOY MILL   20 APR

BAR ¢.91 in²

Alloy Billet = 505 Lbs
EC   = 600 LBS

3/8" Φ =   4200 FPM EC = 32.0
3/8" Φ =   2500 FPM Alloy .125" Φ
                3/8 ⇒ 13/16 @ 1/16"

M - 200 H
M - 200 H

M - 500 H

M -   200 F
M -   200 F

M

M
M   500
           M

6
12
12
12
12
8
8
8
8
8
8

Cutters (2) @ M =

New Mill = 5,68
Original Cost =
Cost

PART IV

JOURNEY'S END

n

nts

nl 2300

$EHP = 1900/P$

$cash$ $\dfrac{300}{2800}$

$36" \text{ ID} \times 48" \text{ OD}$
$34'\text{OD} \times 60" \text{ OD}$
$48' \text{ ID} \times 80\text{OD}$

$\$ \ 3.140.K$

$6 =$

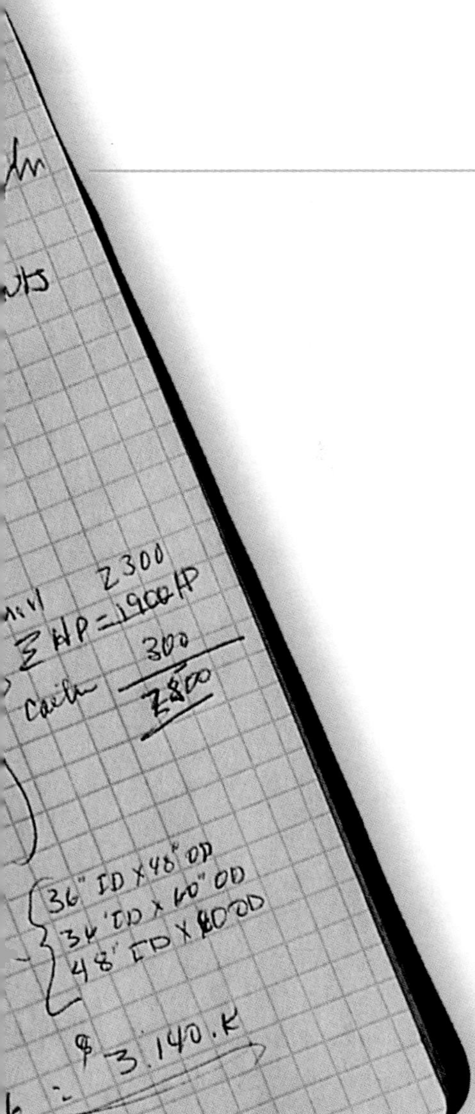

CHAPTER 29

I have no idea how many packs a day Pete smoked.

—DOTT COFER

IN THE 1980s, UNDER ROY RICHARDS JR., Southwire began the long march to becoming the green company it is today. Among a host of safety and environmental initiatives, the copper smelter the company operated in the heart of Carrollton, a source of endless environmental grief was shut down permanently. Another effort focused on preventative health care. In keeping with corporate and governmental policy all over the country, Southwire notified its employees that its offices and other facilities would become tobacco-free zones, a move, remembered Roy Richards Jr., "that Pete complained and moaned about until it was implemented. Then I never heard another word."

Weaning anyone off a long-term tobacco addiction is a ticklish prospect at best. Rather than easing off, addicts—whatever their drug of choice—tend to overindulge as the cutoff deadline approaches. And then meltdown. In the SCR division, Pete's team members tiptoed around, wary that the happy, jocular Dr. Jekyll they loved would transform at any moment into the terrifying Mr. Hyde.

"The no-smoking rule about killed Pete," remembered Milton Berry. "First, it was 'No smoking in the office,' so he'd go out to the plant to smoke. Then they cut it off around the plant, so he'd go for a ride someplace—the copper division, the machinery division, the bank, somewhere. On the way over, he'd smoke cigarettes in the car. The man could not quit."

One long-ago afternoon, Cofer's breakfast-club buddy Harold Miles spotted Pete driving down the Martha Berry Highway adjacent to the Southwire plant. Cofer was in the middle lane, a turning lane. "All of a sudden," Miles remembered, "Pete flipped a cigarette butt out the window of his big Ford and veered left into the plant. There were honking horns, squealing brakes, and a stream of cuss words. Damn, Pete was so busy smoking he nearly ran somebody off the road!"

At home, things were hardly better. Already they'd reached the point where the cost of Pete's cigarettes was impacting the family budget. Never a shrinking violet, Dott put her foot down. "I said, 'Look I'm not taking your cigarettes out of my grocery money anymore. Buy your own!'" Retelling this story, she paused, caught up in the memory and sighed. "I have no idea how many packs a day he smoked."

"I begged and begged Daddy to please stop," remembered third daughter Kay. As a child, Kay suffered a number of respiratory ailments she now attributes to inhaling her father's secondhand smoke. Her bedroom shared a wall with her parents', and she remembers hearing her father's feet hit the floor when his alarm went off in the morning. And instantly, the smell of a burning cigarette filled the air as he made his way to the bathroom. Years later, Kay, then a college student, came home to Carrollton for a weekend visit. To her shock, she realized all her fears and concerns were coming to pass.

"Daddy had gotten really heavy, and his color wasn't good."

Among its myriad deleterious effects, smoking narrows the blood vessels, raising the risk of heart attack; in her father's case, these passages were already likely constricted by cholesterol buildup. The big, nimble man she remembered as "always in motion," had slowed down dramatically. "I just freaked out," she recalled. "I grabbed the phone and made him a doctor's appointment."

The appointment was with Dr. Patrick, whom she remembered as an "old, gruff, mean family doctor," just the person, Kay reasoned, to pound some sense into her father's head. He also happened to be the best general practitioner in town. On the day of the appointment, she made it her business to show up at her father's fourth floor office to accompany him. Pete always had trouble sorting out his feelings, and this time he clearly confused his daughter's love and concern with an attempt to boss him around. On his own turf no less. He blew his stack and, according to Hazel Sprewell and other witnesses, it was an explosion of Shakespearean proportions.

"I begged and pleaded and cried," remembered Kay, who has inherited her father's grit and determination. Pestering him to the point where Pete, the same Pete who could hold his own with anyone, literally grabbed his car keys, ran down the steps, and fled. Needless to say, he never kept the appointment.

On another occasion, the girls grew so worried they took it upon themselves—in Pete's mind an act of treachery reminiscent of King Lear's daughters Goneril and Regan—to call his bosses at Southwire and insist that he was not fit to embark on yet another overseas trip.

"Daddy, they'd pleaded, "Don't you want to live to see your grandchildren?"

"He got *so* mad!" Ann recalled.

In the early 1990s, Southwire arranged for a number of the company's top executives, Pete Cofer among them, and their spouses to visit the historic Greenbriar in White Sulphur Springs, West Virginia, where many Fortune 500 executives make an annual pilgrimage to have their health assessed and fitness programs put in place. The Greenbriar is a four-star resort/spa complex renowned for its amenities, but Pete had his own dim view of the place.

"They're sending me to a fat farm!" he grumped to Larry White.

When the Greenbriar intervention had no lasting impact, Roy Richards Jr., at the company's expense, dispatched Cofer, to the Pritikin Longevity Center and Spa in south

Florida, another high profile "lifestyle-change" venue. Founded by the Pritikin Diet guru, Nathan Pritikin, the spa focuses on reducing the risks associated with heart disease, elevated blood pressure, smoking, obesity, diabetes," a compendium of Cofer's burgeoning health issues.

By sheer coincidence, Larry White arrived in the United States from Asia while Pete was at the Pritikin Center. A fitness buff and martial arts expert, White had his own concerns about Pete's health but knew enough to keep them to himself. "Pete had been in the clinic only a few days when I returned," White remembered. "He called me to meet him, but instead of me going to Florida, he asked me to meet him at the Atlanta airport. I met him at the gate. The moment he got off the plane, he lit a cigarette.

"I thought you were quitting?" asked the puzzled White.

"If the damn airlines didn't have a no-smoking policy," Cofer growled, "I'd a smoked a pack by now!"

White's story is all too familiar, almost a roadmap of Cofer's decline. "My husband was a man who could do anything he wanted to," Dott Cofer insisted in 2011 as she sat reminiscing in a conference room not far from a Southwire research facility named in Pete's honor.

"Anything . . . Pete just didn't *want* to quit smoking."

Another of Pete's SCR colleagues, since retired, took another approach. "Tough old Marine that he was, Pete didn't like anyone telling him what to do. You tell him, 'Lose weight . . . Don't smoke.' And that's exactly what he's not going to do. Jim and Roy Jr. totally meant well, and the facts have proved them correct, but they were imposing their standards, their morals, their personal habits, on Pete.

"Put that on top of his 'I don't think I've got a problem' mentality, and he's not going to appreciate anyone making him a doctor's appointment or telling him what to do about his health. He'd see it as meddling."

Kay Cofer Horton, married with children of her own, is still attempting to understand her father's behavior and its long-term toll on his loved ones. "He was just addicted to cigarettes," she says. "And his health was deteriorating right before our eyes."

Pete was not alone in his addiction. At the time, nearly 450,000 Americans were dying prematurely of tobacco-related illnesses each year. More than eight million were suffering from chronic diseases related to smoking and secondhand smoke. Keep in mind, Pete grew up in a world surrounded by "enablers." In World War II, the military packed cigarettes in every GI's K-rations. The "Marlboro Man" (depicted by actors David McLean and Wayne McLaren) was an American icon—until both men died of lung cancer.

"I keep reminding myself that Daddy had such a high-stress job, a wife to support, and four daughters whom he had to put through college," insists Kay. "That's got to be hard. He was always on the go. Always jet lagged. Always under pressure."

As awards and recognition continued to accumulate for Pete, his health was deteriorating from coronary heart disease. His wife, Dott (above), along with his daughters, urged him to undergo surgery.

CHAPTER 30

Pete, why on earth do you want me to worry about you?

—HAZEL SPREWELL

Because I know it will be damn first class!

—PETE COFER

BY THE MID-1990S, PETE COFER WAS ON THE VERGE of catastrophic collapse. And apparently still in denial. He felt lousy and spent too many afternoons sitting in his La-Z-Boy staring at the television when he'd rather have been out and about visiting with his buddies or playing with his grandchildren. The colds and other commonplace chest infections that other folks shrugged off threatened to veer at any moment into bronchitis or pneumonia. He cut back his smoking dramatically but couldn't quit. He'd even backed off on some of his traveling, swallowed whatever medications his doctors prescribed, made a few passes at the treadmill Dott bought him after their stay at the Greenbriar, but when it came to a logical assessment of his personal health, Cofer's steel trap mind set it aside.

At Hazel Sprewell's 1994 retirement party, Cofer's defense mechanisms were finally breaking down. In a startling exchange with her, Cofer revealed more about his inner state of mind than he usually allowed. He looked fatigued and wan when he came up to the effervescent Hazel, a woman who famously worried about everything and everybody. As she remembered the conversation:

"Hazel, would you do me a favor and worry about me?"

"Pete, why on earth do you want me to worry about you?"

Cofer managed a weak grin. "Because I know it will be damn first class!"

In early 1995, there could be no further denial. An angiogram revealed "major blockages" in Pete's coronary arteries. There was the evidence on camera for everyone to see. Precise, scientific, unimpeachable. "We could see the arteries were clearly blocked," remembered Kay. Pete's cardiologist informed him that the buildup of plaque and other debris would require five coronary artery bypasses. In layman's terms, Cofer's heart was being starved of blood and oxygen, accounting for his lack of energy and a creating a severe risk to the heart muscle itself.

"I urged him to have surgery," remembered Dott. "I told him, 'Pete, you're going to feel so much better!'" Daughter Amy, then living in the Cayman Islands, arrived in Carrollton to help convince her father to have the operation.

Technological advances and surgical innovations had improved the bypass procedure to the point that it had become commonplace and successful. So commonplace that at Piedmont Hospital's underground operating theaters, thoracic surgeons routinely blasted rock music while they carved open patients' chests. Two Atlanta hospitals, Piedmont and Northside, were considered the best cardiac treatment facilities in the region.

The scientist in Pete could no longer avoid the facts. He agreed and grudgingly postponed a trip to Russia. On Sunday evening February 26, 1995, Pete, Dott, and the girls arrived at Piedmont Hospital, torn between hope and trepidation.

"Daddy smoked all the way to the hospital," remembered Kay. "He even had a pre-operation cigarette."

In those fast-moving but indelible moments that mark momentous events, Pete no doubt unpacked, put on a dressing gown, underwent a final round of tests and blood work, sniffed at whatever bland food he was offered before cutoff time, and said what he had to say to his wife and children, and they to him.

At 5:00 a.m., it was still dark when the orderlies arrived and wheeled him away. Typically, he turned inward as the double doors of the surgical suites yawned before him. Whatever he felt was ahead, he kept it to himself. "I was feeling sick to my stomach about the whole situation," Kay remembered years later. "It all could have been avoided."

In the operating room, the doctors stopped his heart with an injection of a potassium solution and hooked him up to a heart-lung machine as neatly as a mechanic attaching jumper cables to a stalled engine. And then they began bypassing the clogged vessels, stitching in the bypasses, lengths of veins harvested earlier from his leg.

The news was good, at first. In a post-op meeting with his family, Pete's doctors pronounced the procedure "uneventful." When he left the recovery room, Ann, Kay, Amy, and Jean took turns spending the night with him at the Peachtree Street hospital. It turned out "uneventful" was a very premature analysis. Almost immediately, Pete began having problems. "Daddy couldn't sleep," Kay recalled. "He kept getting up all that night. Sitting on the edge of his bed, telling me, 'I'm nauseous. I have a headache. I can't catch my breath.' Getting up and up and up. And the nurses made their rounds and the doctors kept saying everything was normal. I just don't believe any of that."

The next night, things grew worse. "Something's not right with Daddy," a panicked Ann reported back to Carrollton. "Daddy's not right!"

To Amy, a registered nurse, her father's symptoms clearly indicated he was bleeding internally. On Saturday morning, Dott remembers "begging the doctors not to discharge her husband."

"Please! Please! Please!"

One must assume Cofer's heart function and other vital signs were normal. He was discharged, despite his family's misgivings, on March 4. Kay drove him home. It was a Saturday, but Atlanta's downtown connector, which links with Interstate 20 West toward Carrollton, was jammed with traffic and construction delays. "Daddy had a memory for geography," she remembered. "The roads were closed, and he said, 'Turn this way. Turn that way.' He took me through the Georgia Tech campus and then to the highway home. His mind was fine."

Arriving in Carrollton, Pete appeared weak and ashen. He went straight to bed. Two days later, he began having difficulty breathing. Rushed to Tanner Hospital's (now Tanner Medical Center) emergency room, he was in shock. Shock is a life-threatening condition characterized by a sudden drop in blood pressure, hyperventilation, confusion, rapid pulse, and other symptoms; it is typically triggered by a failure of the circulatory system to deliver adequate blood flow to vital organs.

Amy's bedside diagnosis had been correct. Pete's deteriorating condition was triggered by internal bleeding. An endoscopy and other tests revealed he'd somehow been discharged with a bleeding ulcer. He was transfused with six units of blood and two units of platelets. And then he developed pneumonia.

Pete's condition was stabilized, but a downward spiral had begun. A week later, he was still hospitalized, now under the care of Dr. Michael Poss. His condition slowly improved to the point that he was able to receive visitors and, no doubt, make a few half-hearted jokes. (In 1978, Pete's lifelong hero, John Wayne, had joked after his heart surgery. One of the actor's heart valves had been replaced with a valve harvested from a pig. Wayne said he felt great, "except for this strong desire to roll in the mud.")

Milton Berry and Frank Jones, then Southwire's crew-cut vice president of transportation, were among the dozens of colleagues who stopped by at one point or another to see Pete at Tanner Hospital. "This day we showed up around noontime or shortly after," Berry remembered. "Pete was in bed. He seemed okay. Then, all of a sudden, he got real fidgety and couldn't control anything. We rang for the nurse." That moment is also etched in Dott Cofer's memory. "I was at a coffee when the phone rang."

"'Dott, you need to get to the hospital right away!'"

Pete had suffered his first stroke. "A cycle had begun," recalled Kay. "They did a surgery to repair the ulcer; then when he was getting ready to go home, he'd get pneumonia or a bladder infection; then he'd have a little setback; then stay a few more days; then finally get to go home. And it would start all over again."

Cofer never considered pursuing a legal action against Piedmont Hospital. He accepted what was happening as fate, destiny, or just an unlucky roll of the dice, inevitable after a lifelong winning streak. Besides, his generation was not attuned to trial lawyers and today's litigious mindset. "Daddy would never do anything like that," daughter Ann remembered.

"Pete had arrhythmia," recalled Harold Miles. "One time, I watched them do an echocardiogram at Tanner Hospital. Pete was throwing off blood clots that would cause these little strokes."

"Pete began to have trouble getting his thoughts together," Milton Berry remembered. For a man who thrived on banter, jokes, and rapier wit, there could be no worse blow.

Pete's chronic disease, a function of smoking, stress, and lifestyle, was now acute and life threatening. Over the next two and a half years, friends, family, and colleagues stood helpless as Pete Cofer's circulatory, respiratory, and other systems began shutting down. "He tried to ignore his illness," added Miles, "and didn't do anything the doctors told him to do."

That, too, may have been part of the old Cofer bluster. Daughter Amy, who lived with her husband and two sons in the Cayman Islands, stayed in Carrollton for months to nurse her father. "He was so sick for so long," she recalled. "I was scheduled to go home in April, but I had to call Tom and tell him, 'You might be mad at me, and you are my husband, but I cannot leave my father. He's never asked me for anything his whole life. I can't leave him now'." Tom understood. He flew up that Easter.

Cofer suffered a second major stroke while attending a business meeting in Columbia, South Carolina. "It was before breakfast at the hotel," recalled Ken Kinard. "He couldn't speak, couldn't function, and was disoriented." Roy Richards Jr. dispatched a company plane and a nurse to rush him home. Richards, who'd lost his father prematurely, was watching it happen again, this time to a man who'd become, in some ways, a second father.

"Daddy recovered, but now his left arm wasn't working properly," remembered daughter Kay. She walked in on him one time when he was holding his granddaughter, Mariah. The baby began squirming, and Pete had to literally scoot off his chair, slide to the floor, and lay the baby down. "That's the best I could do," he apologized. Kay could not hide her tears. The cognitive dysfunction grew more severe. "Daddy knew what he wanted to say," Kay recalled. "If you gave him time, he could get it out."

He hung on, a shadow of his former self. Overseas traveling and doing the deals he loved so much were long since out of the question. When he was able, and often when he really wasn't able, Pete made his way to the office, the need was so strong in him. A Southwire buddy would pick him in the morning and drive him to Jerry's, where he'd eat with his breakfast club. (Jerry, the owner, even baked a hollowed-out, low-fat biscuit specially for Pete.) Then he'd make his way to the fourth floor, where Milton Berry, Ken Kinard, Will Berry, John Durscher, Jim Shadinger, and other SCR team members tried to hide their dismay.

He'd appear at Kinard's door—once the scene of much browbeating—and talk quietly. The two had much in common. At age thirty-nine, Kinard had survived nine bypass surgeries. "Pete asked me questions about my heart problems," Kinard recalled. "What kind of feelings I'd had before my surgery. He told me he'd never had a heart pain, never taken anything but an aspirin before the surgery. I had the distinct impression he felt that he'd been sold down the river. He never said the words, but I surmised, right or wrong, that he was very sorry he'd had that surgery."

In fact, Pete had gone from taking that occasional aspirin to ingesting eighteen different pills a day. Still, when daughter Ann, then living in Atlanta, drove to Carrollton to visit her father, she saw occasional flashes—like heat lightning—of parental concern and the old wicked humor. "Daddy felt a responsibility because I wasn't married," she explained. "When I'd come to see him in the hospital, if there was ever a single doctor or single male nurse around, he knew it. There he'd be, practically on his deathbed, saying, 'Ann, he's single! He's single!' My face would light up red. It was really awkward, but I know he meant it in a lighthearted way. That's what's so painful."

Old habits die hard, or not at all. After one of his setbacks, Dott Cofer raced to Tanner Hospital and found her husband *outside*, looking happy as a lord. "With his oxygen, dragging his IV pole, smoking a cigarette!" she recalled. "I could have killed him!"

CHAPTER 31

Pete officially retired . . . but still came in every day.

—KEN KINARD

⸺◆⸺

IN MARCH 1997, THERE CAME A DAY NO ONE at Southwire ever thought they'd see: Pete Cofer retired. He'd served faithfully for forty-four years, designing and selling the SCR systems that made the company known, respected, and successful in every corner of the globe. Simply put, the man had no more to give, no further reserves of energy or genius, or stubbornness or strength. The year 1997 is a blur in many people's memories, but there seem to have been a number of memorable and bittersweet farewells. Jim Shadinger recalls a birthday party at which "a belly dancer from Eastern Onion somehow got through the gates and showed up in Pete's office. His daughters were there, and things quickly spilled over into the conference room. Pete just enjoyed the heck out of it."

At his retirement party—held at the Cofer Center, a Southwire building named in his honor)—Pete and Dott were literally given the red carpet treatment. The tables were decorated in silver and gold, representing, no doubt, his breakthrough engineering with copper and aluminum. Pete was presented with a globe of the world, a new La-Z-Boy, and a big-screen television, gifts that spoke volumes about his past and present condition. "To Roy Richard Jr.'s lasting credit," Dott Cofer remembered, "he told Pete the office was his as long as he wanted it." Photographs taken at the party show a much-shrunken man looking lost in his new, oversized recliner. His enormous hands float in front of him, as if seeking something to hold onto.

"Pete officially retired . . . but still came in every day," remembered Ken Kinard. As always, it was the work. "He was still caught up. Pete missed the office and the daily challenge." Kinard hesitates, then blurts, "This is a man who came to work the week he died! He was here!"

In the summer of 2011, Kinard was sixty-eight years old, a former bodybuilder whose eyes twinkled and complexion seemingly glowed with vigor. "You can't tell a book by its cover!" he offered while being interviewed. Kinard then announced that his doctors were warning that his many bypasses were beginning to fail. Cheerfully he pondered his own mortality while remembering Cofer:

No one really knows what your psyche does to your physical health. Did Pete work himself to death? I'd say it was the reverse. After retiring, he didn't have anything to commit himself to and was more likely to give up. I'm not saying he gave up, but I'd talk to him quite a bit. We'd have these little conversations . . . my health . . . his health. It was more like Pete lamenting things had gotten to where he wasn't capable.

Capable had always been Pete Cofer's *raison d'être*. And the man sitting at home, gasping in his chair, forced to rely on intravenous feeding to supplement his nourishment . . . was not capable. His daughters, by then grown women with lives and children (Ann was still single) of their own, wrestled with that terrible realization.

"Grumps," as Kay's children affectionately called him, would not live to see his grandchildren grow up; he would not hide presents under the Christmas tree for them, cheer loudly from the sidelines at their games, attend weddings and graduations . . . at least not from this world. "I wanted him to be at my wedding," Ann said in the summer of 2011. But Pete didn't make it that long.

On Saturday, September 27, 1997, a mild autumn afternoon, Kay was driving home from her mother-in-law's house on Wilson Circle in Carrollton. She and her daughters Lindsey (six), Sarah (four), and the newborn Mariah had stopped by Miriam Horton's house for an early dinner. It had been a long day, and the little girls were tired, edging toward cranky. Tomorrow there was a baby dedication ceremony at the First United Methodist Church that Kay was planning to attend. When she reached Bankhead Highway, she had a choice to make: go straight and she'd be at her parents' house on Highland in ten minutes, or turn left onto 61 North and head for home.

"Girls do you want to go see Grumps?"

"We're tired," said Lindsey.

"Yeah, wanna go home!" Sarah seconded.

Kay turned left. And never saw her father alive again.

At 7:00 a.m. the next morning, the phone rang. It was Dott saying Pete had died in his sleep. Dott was long past crying. If anything, the fact that Pete was still living had seemed extraordinary. At 6:00 a.m., she'd found him when she went to wake him and bring his breakfast.

"Kay, Daddy was cold."

"All these years have passed," Kay said in the fall of 2011, "and I still regret that I didn't go straight that Saturday and drop by the house."

When she arrived at church later that Sunday morning for the dedication ceremony, all of Carrollton seemed to know that Pete Cofer had passed. By afternoon, neighbors, colleagues, and church members began to arrive at the Highland Avenue house bearing kind words and home-cooked dishes and casseroles, one of the great and sustaining strengths of small towns. Dott and her daughters no doubt spent the next days in that fugue-like state so typical of early bereavement. There, but not really there; awake, but not fully conscious; forced to keep busy, hold the pain at bay, make arrangements and accept the condolences of friends and strangers, though not feel, never feel, the comfort of their embrace.

Pete's wake was held at the Almon Funeral Home in Carrollton. He would have appreciated some of the goings-on. During visitation, Kay's daughters, too young to appreciate what had transpired, happily crawled around and under his open casket. Mike Horton, Kay's husband, bought a pack of cigarettes and slipped them into Pete's pocket, assuming, no doubt, that Heaven was a no-smoking zone and that Pete would find a way around the rule. After the private burial on Tuesday, a memorial service was conducted at the United Methodist Church by Rev. Allen Howard, one of Pete's breakfast club buddies. Youngest daughter Ann, gave a moving tribute, as did Roy Richards Jr.

Pete Cofer had spent forty-four years of his life at Southwire and, at the end, Southwire was there for him. As his family was escorted out of the church, his colleagues and friends lined the walls of the long hallway: Milton Berry, Harlan Carroll, Ken Kinard, John Durscher, Jim Shadinger, Carrollton Mayor Tracy Stallings, a dozen more, all there to make their final farewell.

One of the visitors who later made the pilgrimage to Cofer's grave was Bulat Abdrakhmanov, the big-hearted Kazakh who was so inspired by the tour Pete had engineered for him and his colleagues at Disney World in Orlando. Along with another engineer named Oleg Chernoshtan, Bulat arrived in Carrollton in 1999 for a SCR users' meeting. "I have asked to take us to Pete Cofer's grave," he recalled. "It took [them] long to understand where and why we want to go. Finally the car drove us to the cemetery. There we laid flowers at the head of the grave and paid tribute to the memory of Pete Cofer. We have learned he was buried as veteran, the participant of combat actions. Till the end, Pete remained a modest man. The memory of Pete Cofer will always be in our hearts."

Life went on, as it always does, in the long months and years that followed. In January 2001, Stuart Thorn, a seasoned executive with wide-ranging experience in finance, marketing, strategic planning, acquisitions, and international business, was brought in as Southwire's president. A year later, Thorn was named Southwire's CEO. The last decade has seen the company flourish, more than doubling in size and revenue despite a difficult economy. Of course, Pete's SCR disciples continue to saturate the globe with his breakthrough technologies. As Thorn often points out, he and his team "stand on the shoulders of giants."

Pete stayed vibrantly alive in the hearts and minds of those he'd touched. The extraordinary life he'd lived and the extraordinary father he'd been persisted long after his spirit had departed. Often, he was waiting there at the edge of consciousness, where one existence transforms into another, just a memory flash, a smile, or a thought, away. And, as with all those we mourn, his passing was a wound that time stubbornly refused to heal. "I still want to pick up the phone and call Daddy and ask him something, or tell him something," insisted Amy Cofer in the spring of 2012. "It was really hard when my sons were young, and they'd do something, or win an award, or say something funny, and I wanted to tell him. But he wasn't there to tell."

One winter's day, Kay and Mike Horton happened to be in the Home Depot on South Park Street, one of Pete's favorite hangouts. "We were just wandering around; Mike was looking for some tool," she recalled. At the checkout counter, Kay happened to glance at a plastic cup stuffed with carpenter's pencils, and the loss came flooding back. "Suddenly, I felt all the air suck out of me. I had this picture of my dad with the little chopped up carpenter's pencils he used to shave with his pocketknife. Drawing lines and measuring off pieces of wood. I just began weeping."

Kay would later give birth to a son, Michael, whom everyone now calls "Cofer." This Cofer is now a lanky, mischievous ten-year-old with "a little, short fuse," she says, "just like Dad." Every now and then, young Cofer will do or say something that catches his mother off guard, that sends the pain surging and the tears stinging her eyes. Playing checkers, he'll shout, "I'm the world's champeen!" mimicking the exact words and phrasing of the grandfather he never met. A grandfather who, in fact, was a champion. A greatest-generation *hero* in every sense of the word.

And who, Kay would like to believe, may well be watching.

Epilogue

WHAT'S MORE INVISIBLE THAN A STRANGER'S FUNERAL?

Anyone driving along Stripling Chapel Road that Tuesday morning in the fall of 1997 would probably have given no more than a passing glance at the small funeral procession carrying Pete Cofer's earthly remains. The oak trees in Carroll Memory Gardens were beginning to turn their brilliant red. Traffic would have been building, many of the vehicles carrying Southwire employees making for the Martha Berry Highway and the plant.

What's more invisible than a stranger's funeral? We began this story with the idea that "a worthy life need not be lived in the public arena." We close by suggesting that Pete Cofer lived a worthy, if not a heroic life. He lived it modestly, away from the glare and bright lights that attract lesser individuals like moths to a flame. Heroism is not a herculean achievement—though Pete certainly had his share of courage and ambition—his awards and achievements are piled like those autumn leaves in the Carrollton cemetery—but rather a slow, often painful accretion of virtue, loyalty, knowledge, duty, compassion, excellence, reaching beyond one's grasp, challenging the status quo, though sometimes failing.

Pete was born in middle Georgia and he died in west Georgia, the span of a mere 150 miles. And yet his life is defined by the most expansive feat of engineering a human can achieve: building a great chain of connection—comrades-in-arms, colleagues, family members, friends, rich and poor, brilliant and simple—that extended to every corner of the earth. So many of them loved and honored him. As a young Marine, Pete Cofer had served as a messenger. Those who knew and loved Pete insist that mission never changed.

A Eulogy for D. B. "Pete" Cofer Given at His Funeral

I always knew I'd be standing here doing this.

When I came to work for my Dad at the company, I shortly ran out of things to do. So I went to see Pete, whom I really didn't know at the time, and asked for an assignment. He put me right to work helping finish the CDS rod mill, and thereafter every time I got stuck or frustrated I came to see him and he coached me forward.

I remember sitting at that round table in his office (which had U.S. patents lining all four walls, photos of all those daughters, and lots of metallic artifacts) and looking up at the quotations there:

"There's a way to do it, better find it." — Max McGraw

"There's a way to do it better. Find it." — Thomas A. Edison

I recall thinking to myself that here's a man who gets on with things.

Now, Pete was the leader of a band of rebels, known as the "SCR Group," and they did pretty much anything they wanted to. He gave them shelter from the rest of the company—including me—and he *inspired* them. Pete was our *Chief Engineer*, which is a corporate euphemism for *shaman*, or witch doctor: someone who knows things, and has seen things, that the rest of us won't ever know or see. There was *black art* practiced on the fourth floor, and Pete was the chief magician.

And all that magic worked because that bunch of rebels followed Pete's wily leadership. They created a company *within* our company that flourished to become the biggest in its field in the world. By itself, it would rank as one of the one hundred largest companies in Georgia. Indeed, I have often thought to myself that *the one person who has done more than any other to deliver electricity to the most distant household on the planet is Pete Cofer.*

Pete, the rebel leader.

Pete, the master of black art.

Pete, our *Chief Engineer*.

I asked him a few weeks ago how work was going. He smiled real big and came right back with his dry wit: "It's great. I don't work in the morning, and I don't *come* to work in the afternoon." Think about that for a moment.

I didn't *really* know how to cuss until I met Pete. Most people would call him incorrigible. We called him hardheaded. But beneath that hardheadedness was a thoughtful, sensitive, brilliant leader who moved a lot of people. And you know we all work for people, and alongside people, whom we respect because of what they do, or their rank, or whatever. But I can tell you that people who worked closely with Pete, as I and others did, did not respect him out of fear, or for his hardheadedness, or for his topmost rank at the company. Rather, we respected him because we loved him: we admired who he was and what he was doing. *Because, someday, when we grow up, we want to be the* Chief Engineer *just like Pete.*

I never doubted Pete's courage; I don't think anyone did. You just knew, knew, that he had been wounded long ago, and had had to face mortality and all of its demons and one's own deepest fears and overcome them. Once when I was facing some of my own, Pete told me the deeply personal story of the most frightening episode of his life and how he had made the incredible choice between taking lives or yielding his own. That is the stuff of legends. That is the stuff of heroes.

He was a father for me after my own was gone. I think he was for a lot of people. And I fought with him like a father, sometimes, and never did I misunderstand his view on things. Mostly, though, we worked together to solve giant, giant problems.

Most people don't know it, but the late 1980s were scary years for the company. We had problem after problem arise, any one of which might have brought it down. And I can, right now, still see Pete screwing the lead up in that mechanical pencil and carefully writing the key facts about the problem in his black book. And usually out would come his slide rule as he made a quick calculation, and then he would say: "Okay, I'll come back to you."

And he always did. No problem was too complex for him; none couldn't be solved. He just broke them down into pieces, and methodically, exactly, solved each one. He was a director of our company, an architect of our corporate strategy, and he was not intimidated by anything. Now we know that mortality was the only problem he couldn't break down and solve.

I can tell you, though, that somewhere up just the other side of the Pearly Gates, Pete's got his slide rule out. He's screwing the lead up in his mechanical pencil and writing carefully in his black book. Because now he is going to work on *that* problem, too.

You see, even *Heaven* needs a *Chief Engineer.*

—Roy Richards Jr.
September 30, 1997

133

Fig. 1

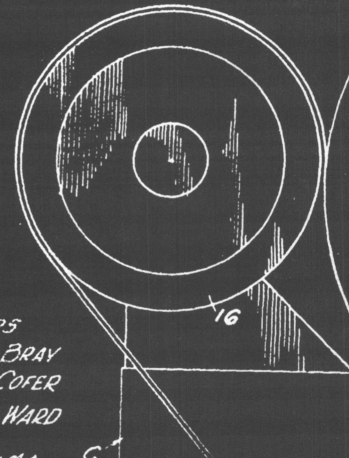

16

INVENTORS
THOMAS L. BRAY
DANIEL B. COFER
GEORGE C. WARD

BY

Newton, Hopkins,
Jones & Ormsby
ATTORNEYS